THE HUNT FOR
GERMAN SCIENTISTS

THE HUNT FOR GERMAN SCIENTISTS

Michel Bar-Zohar

Translated from the French by Len Ortzen

Hawthorn Books, Inc.
Publishers, **New York**

THE HUNT FOR GERMAN SCIENTISTS

Printed in Great Britain

First American Edition, 1967

5000

Contents

167280

Foreword

IT IS well known that in our day scientists have become pawns in the atomic game, slaves or hostages; that they are pursued, kidnapped or merely bought. This new situation is an outcome of the Second World War, although it originated several years earlier. During the ideological confrontation which preceded the outbreak of war, the scientists' role grew considerably in importance.

As it turned out, it was the men who provided Hitler with V.2s and supersonic aircraft who became the prey in the pitiless hunt after scientific 'brains'. Had the war ended differently, the leading scientists of Los Alamos and Oak Ridge would have been hunted down by the victorious Nazis, as those of Peenemünde were by the Americans and the Russians.

I have interviewed the survivors and consulted the files concerning them in Europe, America and the Middle East. Both hunters and hunted have told of the excitements of the chase. As I listened to them and as I collected the material for this book, I was constantly reminded of the fact that our era has seen the greatest upheaval in the history of Science.

CHAPTER ONE

Science and War

The Great Round-Up

It was four-fifteen in the morning of 22 October 1946. In Bleicherode, Dessau and Bernburg, in Berlin and Leipzig, thousands of army vehicles marked with the Red Star were drawing up bumper to bumper in the residential avenues. There was a harsh grinding of brakes, the tramping of heavy boots, then loud knocking on doors and prolonged ringing of bells.

Men and women went down in their nightclothes, still half asleep, to open their doors, then instinctively recoiled – Russian soldiers were standing there, armed with automatic weapons.

Each house had been surrounded. A Russian officer entered with quiet authority, unfolded a printed notice and read it out. An interpreter translated the brief declaration: 'By order of the Russian High Command. You have been mobilized for work in the Soviet Union. You are to leave at once, with your family. Your furniture and personal belongings will be moved to your new residence. The length of your stay there will not exceed five years'.

From five o'clock onwards hundreds, thousands of anxious-looking travellers began streaming into the railway stations. Special trains were waiting with steam up, and their passengers quickly climbed aboard in an orderly manner. Then the trains sped eastwards through the grey dawn of an autumn day, across Russian-occupied Germany and Poland.

A few months previously, passengers with little else but their scientific degrees and a smattering of English had been transported secretively to the United States in the holds of Liberty ships and military aircraft. Attended by stringent security measures, they were taken to special camps in Maryland, Texas and New Mexico.

At about that time, French army vehicles were crossing the Rhine into Germany every morning to fetch some dozens of mysterious persons, who were whisked across the frontier without formalities; and every evening the same vehicles returned them to their homes. During the day they were engaged on secret work in abandoned factories.

Meanwhile, 'transit and selection camps' had been set up in empty Wehrmacht barracks and schools in southern Germany, and in well-guarded buildings in England, such as Farm Hall near Cambridge, which had been the training center for secret agents during the war. Through all these camps passed hundreds of men of all ages who appeared to have nothing in common but the title of *Herr Doktor*, by which they punctiliously addressed each other.

The guns had fallen silent all over Europe, and peace had brought new hope to millions wearied by six years of war; but the hour of rest had not yet sounded for the scientists of the Third Reich. For them, the end of hostilities was the beginning of ceaseless wanderings, of journeys into the unknown and dispersal to the four corners of the world.

All the German scientists, whether specializing in atomic or space research, jet propulsion or radar, were forced or persuaded to take the road into exile. They were later to be found everywhere – on the flat steppes of Russian Kazakstan, in the sweltering towns of Texas, in small, isolated blocks of flats in Britain, in army laboratories in Paris; they were found working for Peron – still pro-German – in the Argentine, for brand-new institutions on the green hillsides of South Africa, at the head of the young aircraft industry in India, and deep in the mountains of Italy ...

The hunt for German scientists had started while the war was still being fought. Soon after the Allied armies broke into Europe, all available means were used to track down these men, to seize and carry off as much as possible of that most invaluable booty – brains. The Americans, the British, the Russians and the French were all dazzled by the realization of the immense contribution that science could make to the means of waging war, and each of the Allies mounted a vast safari on its own account. Special teams dashed about the liberated countries. Files marked 'Top Secret' accumulated in the safes of all the secret services. Plans of attack were modified. Tanks, armored cars and planes lay siege to those strongholds of learning, the research establishments. The Allies' secret services, the German SS, Army officers and scientists were soon engaged in a vast game of hide-and-seek. The prizes were varied – scientific documents, formulas of rare metals, research equipment or just new ideas.

The High Commands no longer regarded the scientist as a harmless, absent-minded professor squinting at a test-tube, or as a man living in a dream world where the secrets of nature appeared as strange equations. Now he had become a potent instrument, he held the key to power, and his paltry test-tube might produce the wonder-weapon which would give its possessor command of the universe.

The metamorphosis of this Professor Nimbus into a fearsome alchemist had been all too clearly confirmed by the terrible V.2 rockets which had almost dealt Britain the knock-out blow. There had also been that huge mushroom of white smoke in the sky over Hiroshima and Nagasaki.

'If only we had been smart enough to carry off the thousand best German scientists and technicians and shut them away on a scientific St Helena, Europe would have remained disarmed for a generation.' This was the bitter conclusion of the assistant director of the American Naval Research Establishment, Admiral Luis de Florez, shortly after the war. Unfortunately, no such clamping down of scientific invention is possible. Is there any chief of state who, in the interests of humanity as a whole, would deprive his own country of the vast resources of human genius? Or any military chiefs who would not strive at all costs to acquire the monopoly of these devilish brains?

Power through Science

Scientists have been sought after since the beginning of history. In the royal courts of ancient times the value of astronomers, astrologers, architects and physicians was soon realized. And while the rulers hoped to gain greater power through scientific knowledge, the men who were probing the unknown forces of nature sought from the rulers the one thing they could not obtain by their ideas alone – money.

Throughout the ages, science and warfare have provided mankind with ever more powerful means of destruction, and yet by some miracle have also brought about a better life for humanity.

In antiquity, Pharaohs, Philistine princes and Assyrian kings all paid huge sums to have the builders of war chariots work exclusively for them. It was because Moses understood the tides that he was able to lead his people safely out of Egypt. And Joshua brought down the walls of Jericho because his sappers had mastered the art of tunnelling and he knew that the shrill sound of trumpets would shake loose the mortar binding the huge blocks of stone. It was Joshua, too, who was able to foretell an eclipse of the sun and warned his people of it, thus winning a battle against an enemy terrified by the unexpected darkness.

It was thanks to the Phoenicians' skill in naval construction that Solomon built up a fleet which became mistress of the Eastern Mediterranean. The conquered Greeks imparted to the Romans the experience gained in the building of Themistocles's redoubtable fleet. Archimedes won his place in history at the siege of Syracuse, when his ingenious arrangement of beams and ropes hurled projectiles at the Roman crews, when his chain-operated crane lifted ships by the stern and then dashed them on the water, and when his huge parabolic mirror reflected the sun's rays onto the Roman triremes and set fire to them. 'It only required a coil of rope or a beam to appear on the flimsy walls of Syracuse,' wrote Plutarch, 'for the Roman soldiers to drop their weapons and flee in terror'.

But the first real hunt for scientists took place many centuries later and on the other side of the world. Gengis Khan's warriors combed the twisting alleys and the gilded palaces of China to bring back to their leader some dozens of slant-eyed mandarins, who were immediately put to work under the iron hand of their new masters. Results were soon forthcoming. When the Mongol hordes arrived before the great walls of Samarkand they displayed a variety of missiles – rockets, fireworks, barrels of gunpowder – all thanks to the Chinese technicians. And the world heard of a new weapon – explosives. From Asia the use of gunpowder spread to the Middle East, where it was improved upon by the Arabs in the 13th century, and finally reached Europe to be perfected by the technicians of England, France, Germany and Italy.

The English used gunfire for the first time at the Battle of Crecy in 1346—it was their 'secret weapon'. Before long, all the European powers were spending vast sums making cannon and seeking gunnery experts who could increase the destructive power of artillery. At the beginning of the 19th century, rockets were used by Sir William Congreve to destroy the invasion fleet assembled by Napoleon at Boulogne. A few years later, in 1807, British ships fired 25,000 rockets to set fire to Copenhagen; and in 1813 Leipzig was subjected to a hail of rockets.

In 1863 a National Academy of Science was created in America in order to derive the best possible military use from the scientific knowledge in the country.

During the First World War, some astounding 'scientific weapons' took the combatants by surprise and wrought havoc on both sides–British tanks, U-boats, poison gas, 'Big Berthas'. These new weapons revolutionized military tactics, and gave staff officers an irrational fear of science and all its works. Credence was given to the wildest rumors. For instance, the British Psychological Warfare Unit put out a story that their scientists had succeeded in training seals as submarine detectors. Commanders of German U-boats soon received orders to kill all seals on sight.

Throughout history, science has always been ready to sell its services to the god of war, regardless of moral considerations. But this cooperation generally resulted from chance or sudden opportunity. In our day it has become a very different matter.

The scientific world in the first part of the 20th century, right up to the outbreak of the Second World War, hardly differed from what it had been previously – a world of elderly professors working within their ivory towers and impervious to the life around them. They proceeded peacefully and unhurriedly with their sole preoccupation of piercing the secrets of nature; they formed a great brotherhood which knew no frontiers, no nationalities, and which had a language and a procedure of its own. It was a world apart. Scientists were equally at home in the laboratories and research institutes of Cambridge, Göttingen, Heidelberg, Vienna, Paris and Boston.

But a few years completely changed all this. At the end of the Second World War the British and American scientists responsible for the making of the A-bomb were torn by a moral dilemma to which there appeared to be no solution. The German scientists were being hunted in the chaos and ruins of their country, they were rounded up, arrested, imprisoned, and then put to work by their new masters.

In Japan, US Commando units smashed to pieces the five magnificent cyclotrons which were the pride of Japanese scientists. In the United States the military chiefs, as though hypnotized by the incredible powers of atomic science, placed full resources and a huge budget at the disposal of the scientists, hoping they would produce the absolute weapon. 'In the past,' observed Admiral Bowen, 'we would say to this or that industrial organization: 'We need a particular kind of weapon for a certain purpose.' And all they had to do was to carry out our orders. But now we say to the scientists: 'Do research in whatever field you wish, and then tell us the weapon to use.'

A scientific evolution had in fact taken place during the Second World War. The invention of radar, guided missiles, the Schnorchel apparatus for U-boats, jet propulsion and the atom bomb, meant that scientists had taken the decisive turning. But it had been a slow process, spread over a number of years and conducted in absolute secret. One of the most crucial episodes in this evolution – probably the first vital step – occurred seven years before the last war, on some waste ground in a Berlin suburb and within sight of a few idle bystanders . . .

CHAPTER TWO

From Berlin to Los Alamos

A Nursery of Young Scientists

In that spring of 1932, things were not going too well for the *Verein für Raumschiffahrt,* an association for experimental space flight. The members of this association – one which would have delighted Jules Verne – had persuaded the UFA Movietone News to film the launching of one of their rockets, hoping to get some publicity and offers of money. On the big day, the rocket rose all right, but the parachute which should have slowed its descent failed to open; and the cylinder of hot metal crashed through the roof of a hut, setting it afire. Unfortunately for the young pioneers in space travel, the hut belonged to the local police, who then called their attention to an old regulation which would prohibit further experiments.

The association only existed at all through the persistence of its leading members, Willy Ley, Rudolf Nebel and Hermann Oberth, and through the generosity of a few Berlin industrialists eager to have an option on the future. As for any State aid, it was limited to permitting the *Verein* to use the old Reinickendorf arsenal for its experiments, for the yearly rent of one Reichsmark.

The rockets which soared above the old arsenal were small, rudimentary things, not much more than toys, that gave much amusement to Berliners who happened to see them shooting up-wards. When the shadow of Hitler loomed over the Weimar Republic, the few industrialists who had escaped the world economic crisis chose to subscribe to Nazi Party funds rather than subsidise 'Utopian' research. The Nazis, however, *at once* took an interest in this panoply, thinking it sounded well among all their strident propaganda; moreover, Rudolf Nebel suggested to the aviators in the Party that they should take over the *Verein für Raumschiffahrt*. This approach caused the resignation of Willy Ley, who made no secret of his dislike for Hitler, and the withdrawal of the few remaining shareholders. The journeys into space seemed to have been postponed forever.

However, one day later that spring a small black car stopped in the Raketenflugplatz – where the rockets were launched – and three men got out. 'Their civilian clothes fooled no one,' said a member of the association later. 'It was obvious that they were army officers.' The three showed great interest in the possibilities of space flight and asked to see the launching of a rocket. The young scientists got busy and prepared a couple of their missiles. But luck was not with them that day. One exploded after a few frantic turns in the air; the other did not even get off the ground. The young inventors were dismayed. But the visitors appeared in no way disappointed by the failure. In fact, they heartily praised the young men and promised them support and help.

This promise was kept. In the next few months the association was given much money and material. But this military aid came to an end in the autumn of 1932. When the army officers finally left the Raketenflugplatz they did not, however, go alone; with them they took a fair-haired young man with bright eyes and a strong jaw – the wonderboy of the *Verein für Raumschiffahrt*, a scientist barely twenty years of age. His name was Wernher von Braun.

The Raketenflugplatz was the last place where one would have expected to find this youngster. His father was Baron Magnus von Braun, of an old family of Prussian Junkers, and Wernher should have entered one of the two careers open to young men of his class – management of large estates or government administration. Particularly as his father was an agricultural adviser in Von Papen's Ministry.

But the demon of space had got into the young man. His first enthusiasm had been for astronomy, but he discovered his real vocation when he read an article on journeys to the moon in a science-fiction magazine. 'The moon was something worth devoting your life to, but not the moon and stars as seen through the eye of a telescope. No, to land on the moon, hurtle through space and really explore that mysterious universe. . . .' This perspective, he told a journalist many years later, aroused in him much the same feelings as Columbus must have had.

No one close to young Wernher shared his feelings, however. He had read Hermann Oberth's book on the conquest of space, but Wernher's teachers considered Oberth a charlatan. Baron von Braun and his wife wanted their son to pursue more useful studies – physics and natural science, for instance. But whenever Wernher had an hour or two to spare he hurried off to Reinickendorf, and by the time he was eighteen he was helping Professor Oberth with his experiments in rockets propelled by liquid fuel. A year later the young assistant was the star of the Raketenflugplatz. He was still under twenty when he signed a contract with the army – the first German scientist to do so.

Was he fully aware of what he was doing – that scientific progress would result in better ways of killing men, and that the fate of humanity would eventually be at stake? Many years later he explained his motives at the time:

> The Treaty of Versailles contained no mention of rockets, so there were no restrictions on their manufacture. The German Army was trying by every means to build up its strength again. As for ourselves, we needed money for our experiments, and since the army was ready to give us this help, we didn't worry overmuch about the consequences in the distant future. Besides, in 1932 the idea of another war was absurd. The Nazis were not then in power. There was no reason for moral scruples over the use to which our researches might be put in the future. We were interested in only one thing – the exploration of space. And our main concern was how to get the most out of the Golden Calf.

The future was to show that the Golden Calf always wants something in return.

Wernher von Braun's Debut

The heads of the Reichswehr had long ago noticed that the Treaty of Versailles did not mention rockets and other inventions which could be put to military use. In great secrecy, and in cooperation with the Russians, work was going ahead on what was later to

B

become Hitler's spear-head against the Soviet Union ...
Meanwhile, a study group had been set up by the Minister for
National Defense to examine, in equal secrecy, the military potential of rockets. The head of this small group was a young officer
with engineering and scientific degrees, Walter Dornberger (later
a General in the Wehrmacht).

In the spring of 1930, Dornberger – having just graduated
from the university – had been attached to the Ballistics Section
of the Armaments Department at the Reichswehr. For many
months, the senior members of the Department, headed by
Professor Becker, had been holding long conferences on the
military use of rockets; and towards the end of 1929 Professor
Becker (another future General) had succeeded in convincing the
Minister of the importance of further research. So the Ballistics
Section had been directed to make a start by building a rocket
with a maximum range of five miles.

For two years Dornberger and his assistants suffered one
failure after another. They made the rounds of all the laboratories
and research institutes, and realized that none of the workers who
posed as pioneers of space travel had any technical ability in this
respect or could be of any effective help. Moreover, the Reichswehr's approaches to heavy industry to collaborate in the project
had met only indifference.

The military then decided to create their own research center,
and looked for the right person to take charge of it. Dornberger
had naturally been to the Raketenflugplatz in the course of visiting all the places where work was being done on rockets, and he
had made a note of the fair-haired young man who had amazed
him by his knowledge and enthusiasm. Here was the right man
for the research center. And so, on 1 October 1932, Wernher von
Braun had entered the service of the German Army.

Exactly a month later, Dornberger enrolled Walter Riedel on
his team. Riedel was a first-class engineer of great experience, but
he took life terribly seriously and was always standing on his
dignity. He was to have the task of bringing Von Braun back to
earth at times, for the young scientist's imagination often went
beyond the bounds of possibility.

The research team gradually increased in numbers, with
engineers, inventors, scientists and veterans from the *Verein für
Raumschiffahrt* (which was disbanded in 1933). Army officers

travelled all over Germany, making contacts and becoming adept at telling real scientists from charlatans. Occasionally they came upon a rare bird, such as Arthur Rudolph, the inventor of an automatic motor, and Albert Pullenberg, whose enthusiasm was equalled only by his poverty...

The new recruits were sent to the Kummersdorf Experimental Station, a secret installation newly built in a clearing among the pines of the vast Brandenburg forest. The buildings and equipment were modest enough, but for the members of the late *Verein* they seemed everything one could wish for. There were launching platforms for rockets using solid or liquid fuel, workshops for draughtsmen, laboratories with all manner of measuring instruments and hangars for experimental purposes. In short, it was a science-fiction setting; and the new recruits, like spoiled children, could hardly wait to play with all these wonderful toys.

However, there was some disappointment first. It had to be explained to the scientists that their new employer, the German Army, had very little interest in the hazy seas on Venus or the problematical canals on Mars. Another Mars – the god of war – was waiting for attention. The army officers set about brain-washing their scientists, and after a few weeks they were ready for the real work.

It had its boring side – long reports to make, interminable conferences and discussions to attend – but was exciting work, and dangerous too. The scientists were literally playing with fire, though they sometimes forgot this; they were then violently reminded of the fact. On one occasion, Von Braun was using a match twelve feet long to set fire to some gas, and caused an explosion which completely wrecked one of the laboratories. Von Braun, Dornberger, Riedel and Grunow, all good losers, smiled when they discovered the mistake which had caused the accident. But they did not smile a month later, when another explosion shook the Kummersdorf Experimental Station. While still in the experimental stage, the war god's rocket had claimed its first victims. Three bodies were recovered from the shattered laboratory – those of Dr Wahmke, the specialist in fuels, and two of his assistants. It was to become increasingly evident that mistakes and errors in this kind of research work could be exceedingly costly.

But nothing could dim the enthusiasm of the Dornberger team.

Work went on again, experimenting and groping in what was then the unknown field of rocket propulsion.

In 1933, the year that Hitler came to power, Kummersdorf produced its first war-rocket, the A.1. In December, 1934, a few fishermen on a barren shore of the North Sea were startled to see a couple of flying comets, as they thought; they were even more startled when, instead of streaking towards the horizon, the 'comets' disappeared into the sky somewhere above Borkum Island. The German Army had successfully fired its second war-missile, the A.2 which had reached a height of 6,000 feet.

'We have made a good start,' Walter Dornberger noted in his diary. But it was only a start, and in order to continue more funds were needed. By using all their powers of persuasion, Dornberger's team succeeded in getting General von Fritsch, the Army Commander-in-Chief, to agree to visit Kummersdorf. When the General arrived he was taken to the launching ground, and three great rocket motors were set in motion. The experiment had never been known to fail, and Von Fritsch was treated to an impressive display of multi-colored flames which was accompanied by an ear-splitting din. It brought the hoped-for result. Von Fritsch said only a few words, but they were what the whole team was waiting to hear: 'How much do you need?'

Dornberger hesitated. 'Ten million, Herr General.' He thought he had gone a bit too high, but in the following months it was not ten but twenty million Reichsmarks that Hitler allocated for rocket research. Moreover, the Führer's support of his apprentice wizards was not limited to financial aid. *He had at once grasped the importance these powerful weapons could have in a future war*, and he issued orders for the scientific resources at Kummersdorf to be increased, notably by the recruitment of more research workers.

Thus a great vise gradually tightened round the German scientists. They had believed, at the beginning, that two courses were open to them; to follow the directives of the army, or to continue their researches without counting on the military or the government. But this second possibility soon faded away. Hitler expressly forbade any work on rockets to be carried out except under the control of the War Ministry. The next step soon followed – orders for the confiscation of the equipment and material of associations for the exploration of space; any members who resisted the order were liable to arrest and imprisonment. Except for a handful of stubborn men who managed to continue their researches by constant maneuvering, all the German scientists were forced to toe the line. The Government's aim was achieved – every worker in rocket research had to knock at the door of military-controlled research institutes.

So the numbers at Kummersdorf were continually increasing; the laboratories became insufficient and too small for their purpose. As the rocket-motors grew more powerful, the volume of noise increased to an extent which could hardly fail to draw public attention to the research station – it was, in fact, less than twenty miles from Berlin. The launching site on Borkum Island was a problem too – an experiment often had to be delayed until the last of the commuters had left. For technical, as well as military reasons it was becoming imperative to find an isolated site where a complete township could be built, where some hundreds of scientists and technicians would be able to construct missiles for the coming war in conditions of complete security.

The Birth of Peenemünde

At the end of 1935 Dornberger sent Von Braun – who had recently acquired the title of Herr Doktor – to try to find the needed site. He visited the practically uninhabited island of Rügen, which seemed ideal for a secret research establishment. But he learned that the Nazi Party's worker's organization *Kraft durch Freude,* Strength Through Joy, intended building a holiday camp on the island . . .

Von Braun spent Christmas with his parents, and mentioned his difficulties to them.

'I know just the place for you and your friends,' exclaimed the Baroness. 'Your grandfather used to go duck-shooting there. It's Peenemünde.'

During the next ten years that name was to summarize the alliance concluded between Science and the German High Command.

Von Braun and Dornberger wasted no time in visiting the place, on the north side of the Baltic island of Usedom. It was a wide stretch of sand-dunes and marshes on which some oak and pine trees grew, and was separated from the mainland by the estuary of the river Peene – whence the name of Peenemünde. There was not even a hamlet in sight, it was a long way from the holiday resorts along the Baltic coast, and this island was inhabited only by wild ducks and a few herds of brindled Pomeranian deer. Some six miles out in the Baltic could be seen tiny Goose Island; this possessed two advantages – a small, well-sheltered bay and a cafe kept by 'Pa' Halliger. Altogether, Peenemünde and its satellite island seemed ideal for launching rockets in secrecy.

The two scientists returned to Berlin and approached the Air Force Command. They obtained a promise of half the funds to finance the new research establishment; and soon afterwards a telephone call from a senior official at the Air Ministry informed them that the Peenemünde area had just been bought by the State for 750,000 marks.

A new page in the history of rockets was about to be written.

Hundreds of workmen were sent to Peenemünde to build office blocks, living quarters, hangars, launching ramps . . . Before long, all the technological riches of the Third Reich began to converge on the Peene estuary – equipment, instruments, rocket casings packed in what looked like wooden coffins – and also most of the intellectual capital, in the form of scientists, research workers, engineers and technicians.

No foreign power appeared to notice that during 1937 several dozen German scientists well known for their work in space research or in rocket propulsion disappeared from view. Nor did anyone notice that Usedom Island had been made a prohibited zone. Never was a secret kept so well as that surrounding the busy hive of scientists on the small island off the Baltic coast of Germany. Not until several years later did news begin to filter through to the Allies of the place where the Nazis had perfected the weapon which came near winning the war for them.

The German High Command had every right to be proud of their achievement of obtaining control over this branch of German scientific research. But it was only a beginning.

Splitting the Atom

While the scientists at Peenemünde were engaged on secret work which was to result in the production of V.1s and V.2s, another group of German scientists solved the great riddle of the atom.

On 22 December 1938, Otto Hahn and his new assistant, Fritz Strassmann, carried out the experiment of bombarding uranium with 'slow' neutrons, and to their astonishment found traces of barium in the bottom of their apparatus. Hahn wrote an account of the experiment that very evening and mailed it at once to the scientific periodical *Natur Wissenschaft*. He also wrote and told Lise Meitner, his former colleague. She was then living in Sweden, having left Germany after the Nazis came to power.

Frau Meitner read Hahn's account with the keenest interest. There could be no mistake, he had certainly found barium in his apparatus as a result of bombarding uranium. How had this come about? What was the inference? She happened to have a brilliant German physicist staying with her for Christmas – her nephew, Otto Frisch. But just then he was more interested in going skiing than in discussing physics. His aunt convinced him of the great importance of Hahn's experiment, and he returned with her to the house. They read through Hahn's account together. This barium, which had not existed at the beginning of the experiment – where else could it have come from, if not from the splitting of the heavy uranium atom? And Frisch, comparing what had occurred in Hahn's laboratory to the multiplication process of bacteria, gave to the phenomenon a name which has passed into the history of mankind – nuclear fission.

Niels Bohr, the Danish physicist well known for his work on orbits, repeated Hahn's experiment – having been informed of it by Frisch – and obtained the same result. Before long, further confirmation came from Leo Szilard, a Hungarian physicist who was living in New York. While in Paris, Frédéric Joliot-Curie and his two assistants, Hans von Halban and Lew Kowarski, made a great step forward in atomic science by producing the first 'chain-reaction' – the uranium atoms emitted energy in the form of neutrons which bombarded other atoms, and so on.

Joliot-Curie's experiment was not entirely conclusive, since the chain-reaction had not been self-sustaining and had quickly ceased; but the inferences to be drawn from it were terrifying. Now that nuclear fission had been achieved, it became possible for tremendous amounts of atomic energy to be obtained. At some future date, man would have the power of destroying all human life. And supposing this power were to fall into the hands of some irresponsible dictator? – a fear easily aroused by the political tensions of the time. Even while the scientists were expressing their jubilation at a great victory over nature, they began to realize the awful dangers it could bring in its train. What ought they to do? Keep quiet and forget these experiments? Put a seal of secrecy on them and never reveal them to common mortals?

It was already too late. Leo Szilard, a clear-sighted man but full of illusions, had at once appealed to his scientific colleagues not to publish their findings. But many of them saw the matter in a different light. Joliot-Curie was the first to disregard the appeal and to make known the results of his experiments. No one could put a brake on scientific progress; it was not the place of scientists to judge the good or evil outcome of their researches. And what right had anyone to decide that the dangers from atomic energy would be greater than the benefits it would bring to mankind?

The ethics of the question troubled the scientific world for some time. . . . The argument was still going on when Hitler invaded Poland on 1 September 1939, and Britain and France declared war on Germany.

The Race for the A-Bomb

No sooner had the first shots been fired than the ivory towers of scientists crumbled away. In Germany, the scientists were promptly mobilized for work in the various organizations and research institutes whose task was to increase the war potential of the country. The 'grey matter' was then utilized to the maximum, and scientists were given definite objectives.

The British revived the scientific research departments which had done duty during the First World War. Meanwhile the Americans transformed their National Council for Research, which also dated back to the previous war, into a Research Committee, and then several months later created from this an Office of Scientific Research and Development (OSRD).

Definite aims for the technologists were: development of amphibious machines, perfecting of bombs and detonators, production of sabotage equipment and tiny rockets (resulting eventually in the famous bazooka). Physicists were employed in research on sonar, a new means to detect submarines, and above all on the perfecting of radar – which, as a result of close Anglo-American cooperation, was to be the first wonder weapon of the war.

Great secrecy surrounded the development of this hyper-sensitive mechanism; scientists engaged on it often went to elaborate lengths to throw enemy agents off their tracks. For instance, one fine day late in 1940 a typical-looking Englishman arrived in New York, carrying a black leather brief-case under his arm. An American suddenly went up to him, and the two jumped into a taxi. It took them to a Manhattan cinema, and after seeing the film through twice they left together for an isolated house where they spent the night. The following morning, being then certain that no enemy agent was on their track, they went to the laboratories of the Bell organization. Their precautions could not be called excessive, for in the Englishman's brief-case was the final link in the assembly chain – a kind of electronic lamp, quite ordinary-looking, called a magnetron. It generated very high frequency oscillations, and when adapted to the existing apparatus it made radar a reality. However, many long months of research were still necessary, as well as much experimental work, before radar became operational.

There was no lack of scientists. So great was the number of professors and technologists who had arrived in Britain from Germany, Austria and German-controlled countries that there was talk in London of 'scientific inflation'. However, whether they were Jews who had fled from the Nazis or opponents of the Hitler regime, all these scientists were 'enemy aliens' and so there could be no question of employing them on matters of national interest.

Some British scientists, out of human kindness or professional solidarity, had set up a relief committee to help their colleagues from the Continent, giving them hospitality and finding them posts in commercial concerns. But the great majority of them were interned in special camps. While the country which had given them asylum could have made good use of their knowledge and experience, they were reduced to idleness.

A rumor went round one of these internment camps, just outside Liverpool, that some scientists were going to be transferred to the Isle of Man, where they would be engaged in research. One impatient young chemist jumped his turn by getting unnoticed into one of the lorries taking internees away from the

camp. But he soon found that the shortest way is not necessarily the quickest. The internees were taken aboard a ship
which, instead of sailing the few miles to the Isle of Man, joined
a convoy bound for Canada. And many months passed, much
paper-work was necessary, before the young chemist was able to
join his compatriots on the Isle of Man.

The decision of the British and Americans not to make use of
refugee scientists in the development of radar had an unexpected
consequence. When scientists were needed to work on the atom-
bomb, the best of the Anglo-Americans were deeply involved on
radar; the Allies were then obliged to turn to the refugee
scientists, and it was they who provided the 'grey matter' to make
the most secret and most terrible weapon of all time.

Early in 1939 Otto Frisch left Denmark, where he had fled
from the Nazis, and sought refuge in England. A few months
after the outbreak of war, Frisch and a colleague, Rudolf Peierls,
presented a report on the possibilities of making an atom-bomb
to the Director of Research of the RAF. This report seems even
more astonishing when read now than at the time, for the two
scientists predicted all the effects of the A-bomb, its destructive
power, the radioactive fall-out, with clearness and exactitude.
Their one error was the estimated cost of the bomb – a modest
million pounds.

The report led to the setting up in Liverpool of a committee
to study the technicalities of making an A-bomb. Very few of the
members could speak English correctly; nearly all were refugee
scientists – Frisch himself, Simon, Peierls, Von Halban,
Kowarski and others, including the man who became the spy of
the century, Klaus Fuchs.

In 1943 Frisch was suddenly called to London and was asked:
'Would you like to go and work in the United States? If so, you
will have to become a naturalized British subject first.' Frisch
agreed, and less then ten days later was on his way.

'What struck me most when I reached the United States,' he
said later, 'were all the marvelous oranges and the neon signs
lit up at night.'

Soon after landing he was sent to the secret township of Los
Alamos.

Frisch and Peierls had not been the first to point out to a
government that the making of an atom-bomb had become

a possibility. In October 1939, a close friend of Roosevelt, the economist Alexander Sachs, had handed the President a letter signed by Albert Einstein which contained just such a proposition. Einstein had been informed of the progress being made in atomic physics (at the experimental laboratories of Columbia University) by two refugee scientists, Eugen Wigner and Leo Szilard – the same man who, a few months earlier, had appealed to his fellow scientists to apply a self-censorship.

It was thus scientists with pacifist leanings who took the initiative in bringing the possibility of an A-bomb to the notice of the American Government. They were convinced that their scientific colleagues in Germany were much nearer making the bomb, and believed it their duty to do everything possible to help the free world to win the race.

These same scientists, and others besides, say today that if they had known where the A-bomb was to lead, if they had known the whole truth, they would not have acted as they did. But at the time, in those anxious days of 1939, it was with a clear conscience that they were prepared to put all their knowledge and experience into the war effort.

Once Roosevelt had been informed, things began to move. The President appointed an Advisory Committee on Uranium, and late in 1941 this became a special research committee under the direction of Professor Arthur H. Compton of Chicago University. Soon afterwards, Roosevelt wrote to Churchill proposing that their countries should combine forces to produce the A-bomb, and that the British nuclear scientists should go to America. Most of the scientists engaged on the project were unaware of its ultimate aim. At the head of it was an affable but determined man, Brigadier General Leslie R. Groves, and the code name given to it was 'Manhattan Project'.

Los Alamos, the Forbidden City

Groves had been Deputy Chief of Construction for the Army for some years, and was an experienced administrator. He was responsible for the building of the Pentagon, the largest office-block in the world. For the Manhattan Project, which had to be kept absolutely secret, he decided to build completely new towns in the most isolated and inaccessible areas possible.

But someone was needed to persuade hundreds of scientists to leave their laboratories, their universities and their homes, and to cut themselves off from the world for a long time, to work under military discipline. Someone was needed with highly persuasive powers, tact and enthusiasm. Professor Compton knew of such a person – Robert J. Oppenheimer, 'the man with intellectual sex-appeal', as he had been called.

'Oppie' was the son of a German emigrant, and had gone to Germany to complete his studies in physics. He had made a name for himself at Göttingen University, where he had studied under the renowned physicist Max Born. Oppenheimer was warm-hearted and highly intelligent, a man of wide culture, well read in German literature, greatly interested in Indian art and with an appreciative knowledge of the Renaissance. This lean-faced physicist had soon become a legendary figure in his own country, with his battered old hat, his mannerisms and verbal facility; his students had the greatest admiration for him.

He had already worked on the uranium program when, in the spring of 1942, Compton put him in charge of the scientists who were to make the A-bomb. Oppenheimer, full of enthusiasm for this great challenge, gave himself wholeheartedly to the task. He and 'Gee Gee' (as the scientists referred to General Groves) travelled about the arid uplands of New Mexico to choose the site for the atomic city of Los Alamos, then explored the neighbor-hood on horseback, becoming quite popular with the construction teams working on the site.

The most difficult and delicate part came next. 'Oppie' tirelessly visited all the places in the United States where a scientific brain might be hidden away. He was not in Nazi Germany; he had to persuade and convince people instead of requisitioning them. But he had few arguments on his side. He could not reveal the true nature of the work he was offering, the real aim behind it all. The only proposition he could make was to do work of military importance until the end of the war, under army control and in a remote scientific centre.

In the end, his recruiting drive was a success. Like some Pied Piper, the sound of his magic voice brought a whole flock of scientists to Los Alamos; and almost without their being aware of it, the walls closed behind them.

They were followed by scientists from Britain, by German

refugees like Peierls, Fuchs and Weisskopf, and the eminent Danish physicist, Niels Bohr.

It had been no easy matter to get Bohr out of German-occupied Denmark. For one thing, he was a perfect example of the absent-minded professor so dear to caricaturists. He would strike a match a dozen times to light his empty pipe; when riding in a tram, he often went past his stop, and then forgot where he had wanted to get off. With such a man, the worst could easily happen – and almost did. Some members of the Danish Resistance went to collect Bohr at his home in Copenhagen, and he had only gone a short distance with them when he asked to be allowed to return. He had forgotten his stock of heavy water, which he kept in a beer-bottle along with the other bottles in his refrigerator. He joined his escort again, clutching his bottle, and was put in a motor-launch which took him across to Sweden. An RAF Mosquito had been sent to pick him up. The crew treated him with all due respect, but had him sit near the bomb-hatch so that in the event of enemy attack he could be swiftly ditched with his Mae West and bottle of heavy water. The plane reached England safely, but the eminent physicist had failed to adjust his oxygen-mask properly and had to be revived. However, he eventually met his British associates and was able to hand over the bottle which he had so carefully carried around with him. Unfortunately, the contents were not heavy water but beer. Bohr had obviously taken the wrong bottle ...

He reached Los Alamos in the company of several security men and under the name of Nicholas Baker, which was of little use in concealing his true identity from his scientific colleagues. (All the scientists at Los Alamos were given different names by the military, retaining their proper initials, and had to address each other by these false names. If an enemy agent had heard that so many eminent scientists were working together in one place, the immediate assumption would have been that something of the highest importance was going on there.)

Niels Bohr confirmed the American fears. A short time before leaving Denmark he had been in contact with German physicists, and he was certain that they were hard at work to make an A-bomb. But no one knew what was really happening in Germany, just how far the development in atomic energy had advanced. It was known, however, that a few weeks after the outbreak of war the leading atomic physicists had been banded into a 'Uranium Society', the *Uran-Verein,* under the direction of Weiszäcker and Heisenberg. It was known that the Nazis had clamped down on the export of uranium from Czechoslovakia; that they were working the heavy water factory at Rjukan, Norway, to full capacity. German scientists had shown great interest in the work being done by Joliot-Curie at his Paris laboratory. In conversations with scientists of neutral countries, the Germans had been very vague and reserved when replying to questions having anything to do with atomic physics; and from this it was presumed that Germany was making great strides forward in the race for the atom bomb.

All this caused much anxiety among the American atomists. Towards the end of 1942 a story went round Chicago that Hitler was preparing to drop bombs containing radioactive material on the city, and this would contaminate the waters of Lake Michigan, bringing death to thousands. Several scientists sent their families away from the threatened city; while others, moved by the same fear which had led them to contact Roosevelt, appealed to the military authorities to warn the people in an official broadcast.

There was only one way of knowing just how far the work on the atom bomb had advanced in Germany – *by going there to find out.*

One spring day in 1944, a Dutch physicist who had become an American citizen, Samuel Goudsmit, was ordered to the OSRD in Washington. As soon as he arrived he was taken to a conference room where the director of the Office, Dr Vannevar Bush, and his chief assistants were waiting. For some hours, Goudsmit was submitted to a running fire of questions on all manner of subjects, on science and espionage, geography and politics. As he was leaving, feeling completely exhausted, a young officer whispered to him: 'All you've got to do now is to run after the bomb and try to catch it before it explodes!'

CHAPTER THREE

Alsos Goes into Action

The Battle for Heavy Water

The mission given to Goudsmit was by no means the first attempt
the Allies had made to block Hitler's path to the atom bomb.

Early in the war, the French had realized the importance of a
stock of heavy water (as slowing material in the construction of
an atomic pile), and knew that possession of it could play a vital
role in a country's war effort.

On 4 March 1940, about a month before the Germans invaded
Norway, a plane carrying Jacques Aller, a special envoy of the
French Government, had landed in a narrow valley in the
Telemark mountains, between Oslo and the North Sea. He went
straight to the offices of the Norsk Hydro Company, which had
just received an order from Germany for two tons of heavy water,
and asked if he could buy all available stocks of it.

The works director, Aubert, was strongly anti-Nazi and at once
agreed to the request. Some 400 lbs of heavy water – all the
existing stock in Europe – was flown to France as a 'free loan.'

In May, the Germans invaded France and rapidly advanced
towards Paris. The twelve containers of heavy water were taken
from the cellars of the Collège de France in Paris and sent to those
of the Banque de France in Clermont-Ferrand. They soon
continued their adventurous journey, going from a prison cell in
Riom to a shed on the docks at Bordeaux, and finally into the
hold of the British ship *Broompark*. Two scientists working with
Joliot-Curie, Von Halban (born an Austrian, but a naturalized
Frenchman) and Lew Kowarski, were personally responsible for
this precious cargo. If the *Broompark* should be sunk by enemy

action they were to take to a raft with their heavy water, and do their best to reach England with it.[1]

The French had also been the first to realize the important role of uranium. Prophetically, in May 1939, Joliot-Curie had put before his colleagues a project to attempt the fission of uranium in a bomb to be constructed in the Sahara. A specially invited guest at this meeting was Edgar Sengier, managing director of the Union Minière of Upper Katanga. He was so impressed that he promised to supply the French with all the uranium they needed.

The collapse of France prevented this promise from being fulfilled. Sengier had left Brussels for New York, where he remained for the rest of the war. Part of the uranium ores in stock in Belgium fell into the hands of the Germans, but the quantities which had been sent to France remained undiscovered throughout the German Occupation.

It was Sengier, however, who took steps to remove all possibility of a large stock of uranium ore's being seized by the Germans. Towards the end of 1940, fearing a German invasion of the Belgian Congo, he ordered his representatives in Africa to ship to New York all the mined ore then in stock at the Shinkolobwe Mine. And so more than 1,250 tons of the precious ore were shipped by way of the nearest port, Lobito, in Portuguese Angola.

Throughout the war the Americans exerted pressure on neutral Sweden not to export its uranium ore to other foreign powers, although the Swedish Government would make no secret agreement, being concerned about the possible reaction of the Russians. On the other hand, the Americans succeeded in acquiring a near monopoly of the production of thorium and uranium in countries outside Europe. The Germans, however, had a source of uranium supply from the Joachimstal Mines in Czechoslovakia. This was a target beyond Allied reach; but they did decide to attack the plant supplying the Germans with heavy water.

During the night of 27 February 1943, a violent snowstorm was sweeping southern Norway. Two small groups of armed men were creeping along the slopes of the Telemark mountains; down below, whenever the curtain of snow was torn aside by the gusts

[1] It was eventually taken to Canada, and was used in an experimental reactor. (Tr. n.)

32

of wind, they could see a few lights in the narrow valley. The two groups joined up and began to descend.

A few minutes later the mountain-sides echoed with a series of explosions; searchlights stabbed the black night and German guards began firing at random; sirens moaned, dogs barked. The din continued until dawn, but the saboteurs were never found. They had carried out one of the most important and successful raids of the war – the destruction of the Rjukan plant, the only place in Europe where heavy water was produced.

The attempt had actually begun four months earlier, when four Norwegians trained in England in sabotage techniques had been parachuted into Norway. Before leaving London they had been told that reinforcements would be dropped to join them at a certain date.

The four men had an extremely difficult time. The Germans had tightened their security precautions round the Rjukan factory; and the winter was proving exceptionally severe. Nevertheless, the four Norwegians were at the rendezvous on time, only to find that the British were not. They waited, suffering from hunger and cold, and in constant danger of being discovered by enemy patrols. At last, London radioed on 19 November that two bombers were bringing two gliders carrying thirty Commandos.

The hope thus kindled in the four Norwegians was short-lived. The bombers lost their way in thick cloud, and the gliders crashed on the bank of a fjord. A patrol of German coastguards captured the survivors, and a few days later they were executed by a firing-squad.

The four Norwegians took to the mountains again. Soon, three of their compatriots, wearing British uniforms, were dropped. It was then the beginning of February. The group made contact with the Norwegian Resistance, obtained food and explosives and then set off in two parties, for greater security. After a week of hard going, both groups reached the summit of the Telemarks and joined up again.

Far below in the valley was the complex construction of the Rjukan plant. The perimeter was defended by barbed wire, guard-towers and patrolling sentries, but the natural surroundings provided excellent protection. The valley was almost a canyon, over which hung a thick hill fog for most of the year, preventing observation from the air. Power for the plant came from the water brought down the mountain-side in great conduits. The laboratories were six floors below ground, the electro-chemical plant being at the deepest level.

Nevertheless, the attack by the Norwegians left the essential part of the factory in a state of devastation.

The news was received in London and Washington with much satisfaction. Some Swedish newspapers, reporting on the action, made apparently fantastic speculations about the importance of heavy water, pointing out that scientists were hoping to make 'secret weapons' with it, notably an explosive of 'incredible violence'. London papers picked up these items, and finally the New York press came out with headlines such as 'Nazi Heavy Water Looms As Weapon.'

All this gave the Allied chiefs quite a headache, but no statement was issued. They were not yet finished with Rjukan heavy water. Information was received that the Germans had speedily rebuilt the damaged plant and resumed production, reaching the record level of over 250 lbs a month – the amount produced annually before the war.

Another raid had become imperative. This time, Rjukan was the objective of a massive air attack. On 16 November 1943, in unfavourable weather conditions, a force of 150 bombers dropped hundreds of tons of explosive on the valley. There were many casualties among the civilian population, but little damage was caused to the plant.

However, the raid had unexpected results. It apparently led the Germans to believe that more attacks would follow, and they decided to abandon the factory. Sabotage by Norwegian technicians working in the plant – such as dropping oil in the precious liquid – hastened the decision. At the end of 1943 all the apparatus, the catalyzers and concentrates used in the production of heavy water, were ordered to be sent to Berlin, together with the stocks of heavy water.

The Norwegian Resistance still had a surprise in store for the Germans. On 20 February 1944, the ferryboat *Hydro*, with the stocks of heavy water on board, was slowly crossing Lake Tinnsjö when she suddenly blew up and sank, taking the precious cargo with her. A terrible decision had had to be made before this sabotage was carried out. The greatest secrecy was essential to its success, so the fourteen Norwegian passengers on the ferry could not be warned. These innocent victims increased the toll already taken in the battle for heavy water.

The Allies had gained an advantage, but were not yet reassured that the Germans were still a long way from producing an atom-bomb. Those in charge of the Anglo-American atomic program were constantly asking the various Intelligence agencies for information on the matter. But none of the latter had a real understanding of what was needed, through lack of scientific qualifications. As one of the American scientists engaged on the 'Manhattan Project' remarked: 'What we need is a very rare bird, rare even in the most sophisticated spy stories – a Mata Hari with a degree in physics.'

The suggestion was taken seriously at the Pentagon. As there were no scientific-minded intelligence agents – why not make some? And when a few had been gathered together, they would be sent into Europe in pursuit of the needed information. The first European country to be liberated would be Italy, a particularly good hunting-ground for these new-style spies. It was hardly possible that Italian scientists, who had undoubtedly been working closely with their German colleagues, would not have some knowledge, however slight, of certain secrets; and files and papers at the Italian universities would surely give indications of the Germans' scientific developments. So the first people to be questioned would be the Italian scientists.

In the Top Secret documents that began to circulate, these scientists were somewhat disparagingly referred to as 'objectives'. And to reach these objectives the Americans put into the field their most extraordinary Intelligence unit, the *Alsos* mission.

The First Objectives of the 'Brain-Hunters'

General Groves, the military head of the 'Manhattan Project', had cold shivers when he learned the code name given to the new mission. *Alsos* is the Greek word for 'grove'. Was this just a joke on someone's part, he wondered, or an unfortunate blunder? He feared the name would give away what he and others were trying to hide – the connection between this highly secret mission and the general who had been put in charge of another mysterious project. However, he decided that to have the mission renamed would only draw attention to it.

Another blunder was made when *Alsos* was given its insignia, its distinctive sign. This was a white alpha with a red streak across it. A more direct allusion to the splitting of the atom could hardly have been made. And the sign appeared wherever the unit went – on its jeeps, the signboards put outside its billets and offices, the shoulders of it's personnel's battledress and even round the necks of some of its officers, who had scarves with the flash printed on them.

However, by exceptional good luck, no one ever discovered the mission's real purpose. Its first unit, consisting of thirteen military personnel and six scientists, assembled in Algiers on 14 December 1943. No one paid any attention when the nineteen men left for Italy, their pockets stuffed with passes and permits, to start the hunt hard on the heels of the leading Allied formations fighting their way northwards. The unit was often among the first to enter a town when it fell, riding in jeeps marked 'W.D.' to show that the unit came directly under the orders of the United States War Department.

Practically the whole of the United States High Command had been present at the birth of *Alsos*. It had been a combined effort by General Groves, Army and Navy Intelligence, the OSS and the OSRD, and was given the blessing of General Marshall, the Chief of Staff, and Secretary of War Stimson. The tiny mission had great importance in the minds of all its initiators. It alone was believed capable of gaining knowledge of enemy progress towards the A-bomb, through its energetic and determined officers, its shrewd intelligence agents and, especially, its scientists. It alone could put an end to the anxiety and incertitude of the Allied High Command.

Every facility was given to the mission. Its leaders were furnished with letters of introduction to all Commanders-in-Chief in the European Theatre of Operations, and the latter were required to give all possible assistance to the small unit – whose real purpose was not disclosed. Its members could also command the cooperation of Intelligence sections with units in the field; and direct lines would be made available to them by Army HQs whenever they needed to contact their liaison offices in London or Washington.

Armed with all these 'Open Sesames', *Alsos* set off to discover Ali Baba's caves.

Clues were very slight. The uniformed scientists went through mounds of papers and documents at Naples University, and in Brindisi and Taranto they interrogated Italians only too willing to talk, but after a month and a half of work they had got nowhere; not the slightest lead had turned up. It was probable that a better harvest could be gathered in Rome. But the Allied armies were bogged down before Cassino.

The leaders of the mission, giving free play to their imagination, made adventurous plans to enter Rome ahead of the Allied advance, to kidnap some important Italian scientists in northern Italy and bring them back to the Allied lines. But neither of these ingenious ideas seemed to have much chance of success, and *Alsos* became inactive. In March 1944, its members packed their kit and returned to the United States hardly any wiser than when they had left.

They returned with the conviction that scientists of the liberated countries of Europe would not be able to give them much help in their mission. Only in Germany could the real results be obtained. The main effort had to be directed to that end. So a start was made when the *Alsos* liaison office in London sent into Switzerland a very reliable and able OSS agent, Moe Berg (former catcher of the Washington Senators and the Boston Red Sox, and fluent in seven languages).

Moe Berg passed himself off as a Swiss student and even attended a lecture given by the renowned Werner Heisenberg, who had been given permission to travel outside Germany on this one occasion. The situation was not without its dramatic side. Sitting only a few yards from the man believed to be head of the German atomic project was one of the aces of the American Secret Service. Hunter and prey could hardly have been closer to one another. The "student" restrained himself, however, much as he would have liked to seize the German scientist and drag his secrets from him.

Berg gathered a useful piece of information – Heisenberg's address in Germany. He sent it to the London office of *Alsos*, and in reply received the message: 'Cross the frontier and follow him. He's bound to go to one of his secret installations sometime or other'. On second thought, however, it was realized that if the Nazis captured Berg they might well extract from him vital information about the Manhattan Project. The risk was too great, the order to Berg was countermanded, and Heisenberg went back to Germany without being shadowed.

Another lesson drawn from the unproductive foray into Italy was that the mission should be headed by a scientist as well as an army officer. The scientist had to have a close knowledge of the German scientific world, especially of the realm of atomic research, and had himself to be a highly capable atomic physicist. He would coordinate the mission's activities and be able to avoid wasting time on false leads. And he had to be someone not involved in the Manhattan Project, so that if captured by the enemy he could not reveal atomic secrets under torture.

This was the point where Dr Samuel A. Goudsmit entered the scene.

Starting All Over Again

Known as 'Uncle Sam' to his friends, Goudsmit was a romantic with a good sense of humor, always ready for the unexpected and little disposed towards military discipline. He agreed to go to Europe on condition that his uniform bear no badges of rank. Friends in the scientific world had warned him: 'The Army will want to make you a commissioned officer, but on no account agree to it! Once you've got a rank, you'll only be able to give orders and talk as an equal to men of your own rank and below. But if you remain a civilian you can refuse to take orders even from a General. . . .'

Not that 'Uncle Sam' had need of advice about talking on equal terms with anyone, military or civilian. In scientific circles he was regarded as something of a heretic for his insistence that there were many other things quite as interesting as science. A colleague once said of him: 'Most physicists have only a current of electricity running through their veins, but Sam has blood.'

This naturalized American was interested in everything that makes life worth living. He was born in Holland, where his father was a wholesaler in sanitary goods; at an early age he had wanted to become an archaeologist, a detective and a scientist as well. Although, in the end, he took a science degree at Leyden University, he also attended classes in scientific criminology and collected ancient Egyptian scarabs. He developed a taste for good wine, and it was through his initiative that the *Alsos* teams acquired the habit of searching buildings and villas from bottom to top – in other words, giving priority to the cellar.

He readily accepted the offer to become scientific chief of *Alsos*; although he disliked the idea of hunting down scientists, a task which would take him right across Europe in pursuit of old associates who included old friends, he also realized that he was being offered a greater adventure than he could ever have imagined.

Sam Goudsmit was undoubtedly just the man for *Alsos*. It would have been extremely difficult, if not impossible, to find another man so well qualified for the job: a capable atomic physicist with a taste for detective work, who knew the eminent scientists of France, Holland and Germany, spoke English, French, Dutch and German, and was quick-witted and energetic.

Such a leader was entitled to a first-class team; and in London and Washington larger, better-organized *Alsos* units were formed, benefiting from the lessons of the past. The utmost secrecy was maintained. Only Allied leaders at the highest level knew of the mission's primary purpose to obtain information of atomic developments in Germany. The great majority of its members knew no more than that they were to 'gather information regarding scientific developments in progress ...' No more than two or three of the scientists, and two or three of the army officers with the mission, knew just what kind of information was top priority. In order to confuse the issue, the team was given specialists in aerodynamics, ciphers, fuses and rockets, and also in biological warfare and radar. *Alsos*, in effect, was no different from other scientific intelligence missions, even to its own members. General Groves was most concerned to maintain this false front. He firmly reminded his personal representative with the mission, Major Robert R. Furman, of this need. 'The impression has been created,' he wrote to him in November 1944, 'that *Alsos* has been acting solely for us. This is injuring both *Alsos* and ourselves. *Alsos* has a definite mission in many fields, one of which concerns us.'

'We created the mission,' said Robert Furman after the war, 'and then we hid ourselves in it. Like building a supermarket in order to sell socks. I mean "secret socks". ...'

These 'sock merchants' eventually assembled in London, ready to land on the Continent soon after D-Day. Rome had just fallen to the Allies. Several Italian scientists were questioned by an *Alsos* team flown in from London, but their replies added very little to the knowledge of Hitler's progress towards an atom-bomb. In Washington, the War Department was worried by the idea that the D-Day invasion troops might encounter a 'radioactive barrier' laid down by the Germans with the fission products from their atomic reactors. A staff officer was sent on a highly secret mission to inform General Eisenhower, who earmarked a special supply of Geiger counters and other detectors. Eisenhower also warned his chief of the Medical Corps, who issued orders for the reporting of 'cases of any mild disease of unknown etiology' – so that immediate action could be taken in case any symptoms of radioactive exposure were discovered among the troops.

Fortunately, these fears were exaggerated. And when the Normandy bridgehead had been secured, advance elements of the *Alsos* mission landed in France . . .

The Hunt Is On

Goudsmit and a few of his men arrived in Rennes on 9 August and at once began to search the laboratories of the university. They discovered a number of files and catalogues that gave them leads to possible future targets. Rennes was in American hands, and the local commander showed great respect for the scientific unit, lending it a command-car with one of the best drivers. But this respect soon gave way to rage.

One afternoon, Goudsmit switched on the radio and heard the emotional tones of the announcer giving news of the liberation of Paris. Goudsmit was a passionate Francophile, and to him Paris was everything, his Mecca. An idea at once came to him. 'What instructions have you been given?' he asked the driver of the command-car. 'To carry out all your orders,' was the reply. 'Fine! Drive to Paris,' ordered 'Uncle Sam', getting in and slamming the door.

The 'car thief' was soon being cursed, but Goudsmit was no longer in Rennes to hear. He was seeing Paris again, the city where he had spent many happy years as a student and then as a teacher, the city he had never expected to see again. Goudsmit was not an emotional man, but he said later that on this occasion he shed tears of joy.

In Paris, Goudsmit made his way to the laboratory of his old acquaintance, Joliot-Curie. There, a surprise awaited him. Joliot-Curie had been in the hands of *Alsos* for the past twenty-four hours. The military chief of the mission, Lieutenant Colonel Boris T. Pash, had 'uncovered' him first.

Pash had been a security officer working on matters affecting the Manhattan Project when General Groves gave him the command of *Alsos*. He was of medium build, wiry and energetic. His parents had been Russian emigrants, and before the war he was a physical training instructor at a Hollywood college. He had discovered Lana Turner, as well as several other film stars. He was destined to achieve some notoriety after the war, as the officer in charge of the investigation into the alleged un-American activities of Robert Oppenheimer.

Pash, with his great drive and initiative, was to perform wonders as the head of *Alsos*. Like some motorized cowboy, he was always ready to go behind the enemy lines, drop by parachute, borrow an infantry company and lead an attack, or play a trick on the enemy and even on the Allied Command. With Pash and Goudsmit in charge, the *Alsos* mission was bound to become a furious gallop all over Europe or, as they themselves had predicted, a 'modern epic of the Far West'.

Early on the morning of 15 August, Pash, one of his officers and two of the Counter-Intelligence agents with the mission had reached the approaches to Paris ahead of the Free French Division leading the liberating forces into the capital. The four waited at the Porte d'Orléans for about half an hour until General Leclerc arrived with the advance elements of his Division. The General led the triumphal entry; and tucked into the column, directly behind the first tank, was a jeep containing the four Americans, the first to enter Paris after its four years of enemy occupation. Later, they broke off from the column and headed for the Collège de France, where Joliot-Curie had his laboratory. There, on the steps of the building, they found Joliot-Curie and some of his staff, all wearing Resistance armbands. That evening they celebrated the liberation with Joliot-Curie by drinking some champagne he had kept for the occasion; in keeping with the seriousness of the surroundings – they were, after all, in a laboratory – they used beakers as glasses, while the American 'K' rations served as hors d'oeuvre.

However, there was other business to be transacted. *Alsos* had found its first eminent scientist, one who had been in France throughout the Occupation and, although a member of the French Resistance, had been in contact with German scientists. Pash and Goudsmit established their headquarters at the Royal Monceau Hotel and spent several days questioning Joliot-Curie. They had to use great tact and extreme prudence in order not to give the French scientist any idea of what they really wanted. It was a matter of bringing the conversation round so that he willingly told them just what they wanted to hear.

Did Joliot-Curie realize what the Americans were getting at? In any case, when two Americans from another Intelligence agency visited him a few weeks later, and asked point-blank what he knew about German progress towards an atom-bomb, he calmly replied: 'I've already told what I know. Aren't you aware that you have a unit here, the *Alsos* mission, which is responsible for that kind of investigation?'

The *Alsos* leaders were quite worried when they heard of this. Goudsmit suggested camouflaging the unit by putting a notice on the office door – 'Alsos Mission, Mine-Clearance Section'.

A number of German scientists had visited Joliot's laboratory during the Occupation. The first had been Wolfgang Gertner, an authority on cyclotron operations. (The Collège de France, where Joliot-Curie had his laboratory, owned a cyclotron.) Gertner was an anti-Nazi and had worked with Joliot-Curie before the war. As soon as Gertner arrived in Paris he had made an agreement with Joliot-Curie, over drinks in a café on the Boulevard St Michel, whereby German scientists should make use of Joliot's cyclotron and his laboratory but only for academic work and not for military purposes. This was a satisfying arrangement for Joliot-Curie, especially as the head of the German Army Research, Professor Erich Schumann, who was also scientific adviser to Field Marshal Keitel, had already proposed transferring the cyclotron and the laboratory equipment to Germany.

It thus happened that several of the German scientists who had spent varying lengths of time working in Joliot-Curie's laboratory were of interest to the *Alsos* mission: Dr Kurt Diebner, who was in charge of nuclear research; Professor Walther Bothe, an outstanding nuclear experimentalist of the Kaiser Wilhelm Institute in Berlin; and Dr Abraham Esaü, who was in charge of physics in the Research Council of the Third Reich until early 1944; and several others besides.

Gertner, considered too lax by his superiors, had been recalled to Germany in 1943 and replaced by an ardent Nazi. Two other German scientists moved into Joliot-Curie's laboratory. After they left at night, Joliot-Curie said, he used to get into their office and check their work, to make sure they were not engaged on research for military purposes.

Joliot-Curie was convinced, as he told the *Alsos* team, that the Germans had made very little progress on their 'Uranium Project' and were a long way from making an atom-bomb.

But this did not satisfy the sceptical Americans in Washington. How much did Joliot-Curie know about the matter? Surely the German scientists would have been careful not to breathe a word of it to him, especially as his opinions about Hitler's Germany were well known. So *Alsos* looked for other sources of information.

There was no lack of sources; the difficulty was to know whether they were any good. The OSS, with astonishing ease, was sending a mass of data to *Alsos* headquarters – names of scientists, addresses, installations. Members of the mission were kept busy dashing about Paris in a car driven by a White Russian, Leonid Capietchko. But most of the time the information turned out to be mere rumor or to have nothing to do with atomic science.

Pash and Goudsmit wondered if they would ever penetrate the veil of secrecy hanging over the Nazis' atomic developments. It was when they were feeling most discouraged that they got their first good lead.

What Was Happening at Hechingen?

When Brussels was liberated in September, Colonel Pash entered the city with the advance forces and set about securing Union Minière's offices and records. He soon made an interesting discovery. A well-known German chemical firm, Auer-Gesellschaft, had opened a Paris office which was run by a young chemist, and his job was to buy up all the uranium products in Europe. This seemed worth following up; and the *Alsos* team in Paris was soon at the office, which turned out to be that of a

43

French company handling rare earths that had been taken over by Auer-Gesellschaft. Shortly before the liberation of Paris, the mysterious chemist in charge of the office had sent to Germany all the company's stock of uranium, and of thorium as well. And thorium, as Goudsmit well knew, went into the making of an atom-bomb at an advanced stage. Had the Germans reached that point? Were they in fact ahead of the Allies?

It was urgent to get to the bottom of the matter.

The firm's employees were closely interrogated, but all they could tell Goudsmit was that the office manager was a German scientist, a Dr Jansen, and his secretary was a Belgian woman, Ilse Hermanns. Both of them had disappeared.

Goudsmit and his men made a thorough search of the office, looking through old diaries, examining used carbons, catalogues, and records of outgoing mail. Their search did not go unrewarded. In a list of registered mail was a letter addressed to Ilse Hermanns at Eupen. This town on the Belgian-German frontier had just fallen to the Allies. Pash was informed, and he said he would set off for Eupen at once – 'I'll bring her back with me!'

A few days later he was on the line to Goudsmit. He had found Ilse Hermanns at Eupen – and Dr Jansen too. The German had been in hiding at his secretary's house. Pash had arrested them both, and was bringing them to Paris. *Alsos* had captured its first German scientist!

Every attempt was made to impress Jansen when he was brought in for questioning. Pash had bedecked his uniform with all the medals and ribbons he could lay hands on, and the scientists and other officers had put on their best uniforms. Jansen was placed facing the window and was bombarded with questions. But his replies were most disappointing, and he appeared to have little information to give.

Pash had brought a suitcase full of papers and documents from Jansen's hideout, and that evening Goudsmit, sitting up in bed, started to look through them. 'I hadn't got very far, when I almost fell out of bed with excitement.'

The reason was that Goudsmit had come across a hotel bill in Jansen's name – and the hotel was in Hechingen.

For months past, the name of this village in the Black Forest region of Germany had been haunting the minds of the *Alsos* leaders. In London and Washington the heads of Intelligence were extremely curious to know what was happening at Hechingen and the neighboring village of Bisingen. These two names had kept cropping up in secret reports.

The first information had trickled through in the summer of 1943, when British Intelligence had received a report from a Swiss source stating that a pro-Nazi Swiss scientist was believed to be aiding the Germans to develop an explosive a thousand times more powerful than TNT; and the secret laboratory was thought to be in a disused textile factory at Bisingen. Nobody had attached any importance to this item, not even the Intelligence officer of *Alsos*, to whom it was communicated. He had filed it away, but that was all.

A month or so later, American censorship had intercepted a letter from a prisoner of war in which he mentioned that he was working in a 'research laboratory which is referred to as "D" in the region'. The letter was postmarked Hechingen. Again, the item of information got tucked away, out of sight and out of mind.

In the spring of 1944 a solid bit of information was received which set things in motion. This was Moe Berg's message from Berne giving the address of Werner Heisenberg, Germany's top atomic scientist. He was living near Hechingen.

British Intelligence worked feverishly to find out all they could about the area. They located a vicar living in England who had spent a long time in Bisingen before the war. With his help, a plan of the area was made, showing all the textile factories and spinning mills. At the same time, other reports were reaching London giving names of several scientists who had been seen in that area.

The head of *Alsos* Intelligence in London, Major Horace Calvert, arranged for the Hechingen-Bisingen area to be put under air-photo surveillance. The first reconnaissance flights, in July, 1944, added nothing to the knowledge of the region. (The pilots who flew these missions were not told the reason, in case they should be shot down and interrogated.) But in October some aerial photographs were brought back which, when examined, gave the chiefs of the Manhattan Project their biggest scare to date. A number of forced labor camps had sprung up like mushrooms round the small town of Bisingen. Within a fortnight the area had become unrecognizable. A complicated pattern of industrial sites had come into being, as though someone had waved a magic wand. Railway lines had been constructed, pylons erected; everything indicated that the installations were being given the highest priority. Was this to be an atomic city, Germany's 'Oak Ridge'?

The Allied High Command hastily prepared plans to bomb this target, but their anxiety was soon relieved. Some British mining experts recognized the installations as nothing more than a new form of shale-oil-cracking plant. Nevertheless, the Manhattan Project people were still worried about what the German atomic scientists were doing at Hechingen. And now Goudsmit had discovered that his suspect, Dr Jansen, who had been sending thorium to Germany, had recently spent several days in Hechingen! Moreover, Goudsmit had come across another piece of paper which noted – though it might have been someone's idea of a joke – that Jansen had been accompanied on a previous trip by a secret service agent with the incredible name of Haroun Al-Rachid Bey . . .

Goudsmit was too excited and worried to get much sleep that night. In the morning he had Jansen brought to his office, and he prepared to drag from the German all he knew. But Jansen said he had not seen anything remarkable at Hechingen, and had gone there for one reason only – to see his aged mother. When pressed about this, he produced letters, rail tickets and various papers to prove that his mother really did live in Hechingen. He persisted that he had had no other motive for going there, after his journey to Berlin, and from Hechingen he had travelled on to Eupen to see his secretary, Ilse Hermanns. He seemed more astonished than Goudsmit and the others who were questioning him, and maintained that the only unusual thing he had noticed at Hechingen was the influx of refugees.

Then how about the thorium? The reply to this, supported by many documents and by his secretary, was so unexpected and astonishing that the *Alsos* men did not know whether to laugh or to cry.

The managers of the Auer-Gesellschaft had not expected the war to go on forever, bringing the company large profits from the manufacture of gas-masks and chemicals, and they had wisely looked round for some product which was likely to command a wide market in peacetime. They finally settled on one which seemed to have a great commercial future – dentifrice. And they had even taken out a patent for a new kind of toothpaste and chosen a publicity slogan for it: 'Use toothpaste containing thorium and your teeth will sparkle with a radioactive gleam!'

So the mystery about the thorium was cleared up. Instead of going into the construction of an atom-bomb, it was being stocked to flood the postwar market with a harmless dentifrice. Once again, the chiefs of the Manhattan Project breathed freely; and once again the *Alsos* mission was back where it had started.

Operation Jackpot

Goudsmit was very depressed by the Jansen affair, and wondered if the mission would ever discover anything of real importance. He received a visit from Dr Vannevar Bush, the chairman of the OSRD (Office for Scientific Research and Development) who was making a tour of the liberated countries of Europe. Soon after Bush left Paris, an urgent despatch arrived from Colonel Pash. It informed Goudsmit that his colleague was in Strasbourg, which had just been liberated, and he had succeeded in capturing several German scientists – some of them atomic physicists.

Goudsmit left at once for Strasbourg, once more full of optimism. He felt sure that he was on the right track this time, and that his journey to Alsace would bring great success.

Colonel Pash and his advance party had been among the first to enter Strasbourg with the Task Force of the American Sixth Army Group. It was a cold morning, 25 November, and the Germans were still shelling the city from the other side of the Rhine. Pash and his men had learned its layout by heart; they went at once to the university and took over the laboratories and offices. While some of the agents began examining documents and correspondence, others hurried off hoping to arrest some of the German scientists at their addresses discovered in the offices.

But none of the Germans was found, either at the university or at their home addresses. The leading German physicist, Professor C.F.F. von Weizsäcker, was known to have recently joined the staff at Strasbourg University; but judging by the dust in his office he must have left before the entry of the Allied forces.

The *Alsos* team knew from catalogues and documents

discovered in Paris that the Nazis had treated Strasbourg University as an entirely German institution; it was staffed by Germans, the best scientific equipment had been sent there and the faculty was working on war projects. Dr Fleischmann, another well-known physicist, was believed to be at Strasbourg. And a report had been received from Dutch sources that some ultramodern equipment had recently been sent to Strasbourg from the Philips works at Eindhoven.

Where could the people engaged on all this research be hiding? The Gauleiter had been proclaiming to the population until the very last moment that the city was in no danger. So it appeared extremely unlikely that the 'long-haired brains', as the *Alsos* leaders referred to the scientists, had been evacuated or had fled. Nevertheless, no trace of them could be found.

Pash had not given up, and an item of news which came his way had set him thinking. There were said to be a great many doctors at Strasbourg hospital, an inordinate number of them. Pash sent a team to investigate.

This time, the trail led to their quarry. In one wing of the hospital the *Alsos* agents found a heap of apparatus which had little resemblance to any surgical equipment; and some white-clad doctors were wandering about the corridors, apparently not too happy at meeting Allied soldiers. The *Alsos* men, sensing that they were on to something, arrested a number of these doctors. By evening, they had established that among them were seven physicists and chemists, of whom four were well-known nuclear physicists. One of the latter was Dr Fleischmann. He had not seemed at all pleased at being freed from the 'Nazi yoke'. When the Americans began to question the scientists, Fleischmann had at once turned towards his colleagues and told them, sharply and with authority, what attitude they should adopt. At one point, he even ordered them to refuse to answer questions on any important subjects. Pash was not having this, and decided to separate Fleischmann from the others; he was put in a cell at the city jail, without any consideration for his status and learning.

Goudsmit went to see him there, soon after arriving from Paris. Goudsmit wrote:

It was an odd sensation, visiting the German scientists we now held under arrest. These were some of the men I had been looking for, German nuclear physicists. Yet I felt uncertain of myself and even somewhat embarrassed in their presence, especially at the prospect of calling on a colleague in jail. How was I certain he deserved to be in jail? Or was this just normal in war? The physicists in Strasbourg did not know who we were or what we were after and I did not tell them until several days later.[2]

Goudsmit must have felt strange telling the German scientists that he belonged, like them, to the great brotherhood of physicists. He was beginning to doubt, there in Strasbourg jail, whether that brotherhood was still intact. Scientists had really been a community, bound together by their research and proud that it knew no frontiers. But would that community spirit survive the war? The mutual distrust of American and German scientists at their first contact convinced Goudsmit that the warlords had succeeded in turning the 'long-haired brains' into passive tools.

Subsequent questioning of Fleischmann and his colleagues brought no result. The Germans remained tight-lipped and hostile, and their answers failed to provide the *Alsos* team with any useful information. There remained only one slight hope – the documents and personal correspondence captured at the university.

That evening, Goudsmit and his right-hand man, Fred Wardenburg, had a quick meal and then, although tired, settled down in Von Weizäcker's study at the university to go through the mass of papers. Goudsmit wrote later, in his book:

It was a rough evening. The Germans were shelling the city from across the river; our guns were answering. Air raids and air battles raged overhead. We had no light but a few candles and a compressed gas lamp. In the center of the room, our soldiers were playing cards. Fred and I sat in a corner on easy chairs and began to scan the German files.

We both let out a yell at the same moment, for we had both found papers that suddenly raised the curtain of secrecy for us.[3]

---

[2] Samuel A. Goudsmit, *Alsos* (New York: Henry Schuman, Inc., 1947), pp. 67-68
[3] Goudsmit, *Alsos*, pp. 68-69.

C

According to other accounts, one of the GI's cried, 'Have you won the jackpot, doctor?' 'It looks like it,' said Goudsmit. 'We'll soon win the war now.' 'I knew we'd make it,' commented the other GI, and went on calmly playing cards.

If Goudsmit had not quite won the war, he had at least won a battle. In a matter of hours, he uncovered a veritable mine of information in Weiszäcker's papers. For two days and nights, he and Wardenburg went through the notes of meetings, scraps of reports and fragments of computations, the letters and type-written descriptions of experiments, until their eyes were red with fatigue and their faces haggard from lack of sleep. They did not discover any secret reports of direct research on nuclear weapons. But from the private correspondence between Weiszäcker and Heisenberg, reports of experiments and notes hurriedly made, there emerged a revealing picture of nuclear research in Germany.

The German scientists, it appeared, were still having great difficulty in separating uranium isotopes. Their first experimental uranium pile had only recently been achieved – in August, 1944 – whereas the Americans had reached that point in 1940!

Goudsmit gleefully made out his report and sent it in great triumph to Washington. The terrifying spectre of a German atomic attack had evaporated. The Nazis would not possess a nuclear weapon for several years yet, and in the meantime ...

Goudsmit and the others returned to Paris, highly satisfied with the results of Operation Jackpot, as they had named it. They took the four German physicists back with them for further questioning and possible transfer to the United States. These prisoners, who were still unaware of the real nature of *Alsos,* could not understand why their captors were in such holiday mood all the way to Paris. They maintained their haughty air, convinced as they were of the supremacy of German atomic physics. This made the Americans even happier. Goudsmit relaxed into pleasant musings. 'Now that the States are in no danger from a German A-bomb, they'll leave their own in cold storage,' he told himself. But his illusions were soon shattered. A few weeks later he met Major Furman, the officer who had revealed to him the real purpose of the *Alsos* mission. 'Don't deceive yourself, Sam,' Furman said to him. 'If we have such a weapon, we shall use it for sure.'

The *Alsos* team regarded the operation at Strasbourg as most successful and one which fully justified the mission's existence. They had captured important scientists and documents, and had been able to reassure the Pentagon. So Goudsmit was far from expecting the severe reprimand that awaited him in Paris.

The cause of it went back to September and to what almost amounted to an act of heroism. The dare-devil of the mission, Captain Blake, had been attached to the American forces advancing towards the Rhine, and his special task was simply to fill a few bottles with water from the river and take them back to Paris. The reason for this was that Washington suspected the existence of German experimental piles in research establishments near the Rhine, and thought that its waters were being used as a cooling element. If this were so, there would be traces of radioactivity in the water.

As soon as Allied forces had reached the Rhine on a narrow front, Captain Blake hastened to the area and, under enemy fire, filled his bottles. He returned to Paris, where the bottles were carefully packed and despatched at once to Washington. Major Furman, with a thought for his chairborne colleagues on the other side of the Atlantic, added to the parcel a bottle of wine from the Roussillon. On it, he stuck a label with the words 'Radioactivity also to be checked.' That, he thought, was good for a laugh.

A few days later a Top Secret cable from Washington had reached the *Alsos* office in Paris. It was quickly decoded and was found to read: 'Wine radioactive. Send more. Immediate execution.'

Furman and Goudsmit took it in good humor. The wine, they told each other, had obviously been appreciated. And now Washington was carrying on the joke.

But it was no joke. A second and then a third cable were received. Furman had to admit that his Washington colleagues must have taken his label seriously; they had tested the wine instead of drinking it. And now they appeared to think that the Germans might have set up a laboratory for atomic research among the vineyards of the Roussillon. Goudsmit soon received an order: 'Send someone at once to inspect the region that produced the irregular wine.'

Goudsmit was furious. How was he to explain to those stupid

bureaucrats in Washington that French water is sometimes slightly radioactive? Besides, it was no time to be sending an officer to the south of France; the liberation of Strasbourg was imminent, and *Alsos* would need to be at full strength for the work undoubtedly waiting for them there. But Goudsmit could not do otherwise than carry out the order. He sent for the physicist who had 'won' the bottle of Roussillon soon after landing with the Allied forces in the south of France. Goudsmit told this officer, Major Russell A. Fisher, that he was being sent down to Marseilles with another officer, Captain Wallace Ryan, to bring back some more bottles of the same wine.

'Make a good job of it, and don't be stingy with your expense account,' Goudsmit said to them before they left (he probably had ideas of getting his own back). 'See that our Paris office gets a couple of bottles of each sample.'

Nothing was heard from Fisher and Ryan for ten days. Then, one memorable evening, the 'vineyard commando' arrived back in merry mood, loaded down with luggage that showed they had faithfully carried out their instructions.

They had quite a story to tell. The wine-growers and merchants in the south had taken them for Americans in the wine trade who were seizing an opportunity to get in first and start negotiations for business concessions. They were treated royally wherever they went, given free sample bottles of every wine they showed an interest in, and were invited to banquets at which they drank prodigious quantities of red, white and *rosé* wines. The ten days spent in the south had been a continuous feast, worthy of Bacchus. However, in addition to collecting many bottles of excellent wines, they had gathered samples of grapes, of soil from vineyards and water from rivers and streams; and all had been painstakingly classified, labelled and packed.

It was all sent – minus the second sample bottle of each wine – to Washington, together with a long and amusing report made out by Major Fisher.

The arrival of this package had put a stop to the flow of urgent and Top Secret cables. But when Goudsmit arrived back in Paris from Strasbourg, feeling naturally proud of his work there, he found a cold shower waiting for him instead of warm congratulations. His superiors reminded him in the sharpest terms that the atom-bomb was not a fit subject for joking.

However, the *Alsos* leaders had no time to philosophize about their chairborne superiors' lack of a sense of humor. The chiefs of the Manhattan Project were as skeptical and anxious as ever, and were by no means reassured by the documents and correspondence captured at Strasbourg University. Might not these papers have been planted, with the intention of reducing Allied vigilance? The only way of calming down and satisfying the Generals in the Pentagon was to capture the secret laboratories at Hechingen and all the German scientists capable of making a nuclear weapon.

Alsos prepared for its next campaign, which promised to be more difficult, more exciting, and more dangerous too, than any previous activities. But the mission was now in possession of much dependable information for its future operations. The scientist-hunters even had Heisenberg's home address, which Goudsmit had found on a crumpled carbon in Weiszäcker's wastepaper-basket.

The name of Heisenberg alone was enough to give the Manhattan Project chiefs the shivers. And urgent cables kept reminding *Alsos* of its chief task when it crossed the Rhine and entered Germany – 'Arrest Heisenberg'.

CHAPTER FOUR

Treasure Hunt

Beating the French to It

If a photographer had managed to slip into a certain office in the Pentagon one sunny afternoon in April, 1945, he could have taken one of World War Two's most comic pictures. Four men, apparently in full possession of their faculties, were prowling along on their hands and knees peering at the bottom of a huge wall map. They were none other than Henry Stimson, Secretary of War; his aide, Colonel William H. Kyle; the Chief of Staff, General Marshall, and General Groves, military chief of the Manhattan Project.

What were they looking for at the bottom of this huge map?

German resistance was crumbling and the Allied armies were thrusting deep into the interior. Towns were falling in rapid succession. Yet the four Americans were concentrating their attention on finding the name of a small town in southern Germany – Hechingen – which had already appeared in many Intelligence reports.

When General Groves had heard that Germany was to be divided into four zones of occupation instead of the three arranged at Yalta, he could see that he had another problem on his hands. Because the fourth, the French zone, was to be taken from the Americans' slice of the German cake; and it contained the two villages of Hechingen and Bisingen, as well as Haigerloch, where the Germans were believed to have moved their experimental uranium pile, and where unusual activity had been revealed by Allied aerial reconnaissance. These three places were now in the French Army's line of advance, far removed from the zone of any American unit.

Groves and Marshall had pleaded in vain for this small sector to be retained in the American zone; but the State Department representatives who re-partitioned the zones refused to go along with them without a full explanation of their reasons. This Groves and Marshall would not give; the closely guarded secret had to be kept. Instead, a drastic measure was planned.

Groves had become convinced that Joliot-Curie was a Communist, and that if the French came across the German atomic secrets they would hand them to the Russians on a plate. So the Americans had to beat the French to them. Groves had accordingly discussed the matter with General Marshall, and then the two went to see the Secretary of War.

When they finally located Hechingen at the bottom of that large map, and had studied the approaches to the area, Secretary Stimson agreed that a military intervention was necessary. It was given a code name there and then – Operation Harborage. A plan for capturing the objectives was drawn up: a reinforced corps would cut diagonally across the advancing French front, seize Hechingen and occupy the area before the French had time to wonder what American troops were doing there.

Groves sent one of his officers, Major Lansdale, to Allied Supreme HQ (SHAEF) at Rheims to make the necessary arrangements. Lansdale reported to General Bedell Smith, who gave full cooperation and promised to detach one airborne and one armored division for Harborage.

All that *Alsos* had to do was to await the moment for launching this surprise-thrust.

Uranium as Booty

The early months of 1945 saw a series of triumphs for the *Alsos* mission. Divided into small teams, some no more than two men in a jeep, they dashed about France, Holland and Germany, forcing all doors, penetrating laboratories, discovering secret factories, capturing huge stocks of uranium ore, cases of documents and scientists in hiding.

Following information received from Brussels, Pash and some of his men had gone into the front lines of the British sector and, under sniper fire, recovered sixty-eight tons of uranium ore –

without revealing to the British the purpose of their mission. The ore had then been removed from Belgium and shipped to the United States.

They had hardly completed that task when they were ordered to search for more uranium ore in the south of France. (This was the ore sent by the Union Minière early in the war, which had remained concealed from the Germans throughout the Occupation.) The *Alsos* men were hindered in their search by thousands of German troops who were roaming the countryside south of the river Loire, having been cut off by the advance of the American Seventh Army. But *Alsos* found thirty tons of the ore near Toulouse. They saw no reason to inform the French authorities, and this booty followed the other across the Atlantic.

The biggest haul, however, was made in Germany, with British participation. It was well worth the effort, since it consisted of the whole of the German stock of uranium ore – eleven hundred tons. This huge treasure had been hidden in a salt mine near Stassfurt, which lay between the American and Russian armies. Brigadier General E. L. Sibert, G.2 (Intelligence) of the Twelfth Army Group, was somewhat hesitant about the operation. 'What will our Russian allies say?' he kept asking. But General Bradley reassured him with the terse comment, 'To hell with the Russians!'

Accordingly, one day early in 1945, an odd-looking unit was seen passing through the Allied lines. Among the British and American officers was one who had seized the opportunity to put on his colonel's uniform of his First World War regiment, the Coldstream Guards. He was Sir Charles Hambro, who had been a British delegate to the Manhattan Project. The other British with him were civilian scientists, but dressed in officers' uniforms.

This group had no difficulty in locating and seizing the uranium ore. The problem was how to pack it and then move it. The Americans, with their usual resourcefulness, found a barrel factory in the neighborhood and prevailed upon the owner, who was the local burgomaster, to do the conquering Allies a favor. He got hold of some of his workmen, and in two weeks they turned out twenty thousand barrels. Then a truck company of hefty Negro GIs got to work, and soon there were long convoys of lorries trundling the ore back to an airfield in the American sector. From there it was flown to England and eventually sent over to the United States.

The route for the convoys to take to the airfield had been well marked by signposts, which for this operation bore the name 'Calvert' (after the head of *Alsos* Intelligence in London, who had joined the hastily formed group). This name roused the curiosity of troops in the area, and led to much speculation. For the Americans, with a taste for strong drink, 'Calvert' was a well-known brand of whisky and meant that undreamed-of quantities had been found. The British, noting the color of the ore and the presence of Hambro, well-known as a member of a family of City bankers, had a different explanation. 'Nothing to do with whisky,' they said knowingly. 'It's gold.'

For Major Calvert, this 'uranium crusade' was the crowning achievement of a wartime career as head of the *Alsos* liaison office in London. In a few months between his arrival in London, in January, 1944, and the opening of the Second Front he had worked wonders. He first assured the cooperation of American Military Intelligence, then of the American Embassy and finally of the British Atomic Energy Office; and acquired a desk at all three places. Once he was established, Calvert communicated with the War Department in Washington through the American Embassy in London – in top secret code, of course, and with key-words coded again. In fact, the Americans had a mania for giving code-words to everything, usually by drawing upon the names of their States. Thus the exotic names of Utah and Omaha achieved lasting fame in Europe because they were used as code words for landing beaches in the Normandy invasion. In messages to and from Calvert, 'New York' stood for uranium, 'Indiana' for plutonium and 'Nevada' for British intelligence.

Calvert, however, soon became more concerned with another list of names – a list of German scientists, with their addresses. At first he managed to collect fifty, then he added to his information. His colleagues in the United States were told to ask the refugee scientists – among them Otto Frisch, Niels Bohr and Enrico Fermi – to furnish all the details they could on their friends and colleagues still in Europe. In Switzerland, Sweden and other neutral countries, anti-Nazi scientists were likewise questioned. Allied Intelligence agencies scanned German newspapers that had been smuggled out, searching for the slightest clue to the whereabouts and movements of German scientists. Scientific journals from Germany were also scrutinized, the wily notion being that specialists absent from the lists of contributors were probably the ones doing the most important work.

This painstaking detective work enabled the *Alsos* mission to land in Europe armed with a mass of information on German research scientists. It also had detailed lists of every metal refinery, industrial plant and laboratory which might conceivably have some connection with Hitler's atomic projects. All plants where work of an unknown nature was going on, and all uranium mines and storage points, were constantly checked by aerial reconnaissance.

A special method was adopted for the Joachimsthal mines in Czechoslovakia, which were the main source of Hitler's uranium ore supply. Periodical reconnaissance flights were made over the mining area; RAF pilots risked their lives to dive low and take great numbers of photographs, which were later studied in detail by experts. Piles of ore were microscopically measured, the height being calculated by the shadow they cast. By making comparisons from one reconnaissance to the next, experts were able to estimate the rate of the mine's production.

The Americans were particularly provoked by a series of aerial photographs taken at the end of 1944. They were of the Auer-Gesellschaft works (already known to *Alsos* as prospective manufacturers of thorium toothpaste). It was plain from the photos that these works at Oranienburg, about fifteen miles north of Berlin, were processing all the uranium ore from the mines still held by the Germans. As the town lay in what was to be the Russian zone, the American High Command did not hesitate to destroy the works by air attack. On 15 March, 1945, General Carl Spaatz sent 612 Flying Fortresses of the Eighth Air Force to drop 1,506 tons of high explosives and 178 tons of incendiary bombs on Oranienburg. The works were completely destroyed. To screen the purpose of the raid from the Russians, a heavy air attack was simultaneously delivered on the small town of Zossen, where the Wehrmacht High Command was situated. No special result was expected from this diversionary attack, but it put the Chief of the German General Staff, General Guderian, out of action.

Where to Make a Start?

While the bombers were over Oranienburg, *Alsos* was entering Heidelberg. This was the culmination of a series of adventurous episodes. Near Verdun, for instance, an *Alsos* team had come upon an underground factory where thousands of slave laborers were controlled by some five hundred Germans. At the approach of the American forces, the Germans had massacred dozens of their slaves – some were barely fourteen years of age – and then fled after blowing up the entrances to the factory. It was one of the places where the Germans were making their 'reprisal weapons', as they called them – the frightening V.1s, or 'doodle-bugs'.

Another *Alsos* team, consisting only of Dr Allan Bates and his driver, had succeeded in putting a stop to the looting and disorders being committed in a small German town by some of the hordes of 'displaced persons' who had broken free from the slave labor and concentration camps and were roaming the countryside. The two Americans had coolly enlisted the aid of some escaped French p.o.w.'s, and supplied them with weapons. When order was restored in the town, its leading citizens presented Bates – whom they addressed as 'Herr General' – with the town's most treasured possession, a sword which had belonged to Napoleon.

Goudsmit had no sooner arrived in Heidelberg than he was accosted by a very excited American officer. 'Professor Goudsmit,' he panted, 'an old man has just given himself up. He claims to be the greatest scientist in the whole of Germany. His name is Lenard.'

Goudsmit knew the name well. Lenard had been an outstanding physicist in his younger days and had won the Nobel Prize in 1905. Later he had gone into politics, and was said to have been a Nazi long before the advent of Hitler. He had campaigned against the Weimar Republic, and had forbidden the use of his laboratory to Jewish research-workers. The more he dabbled in politics the less time he gave to science, which did not prevent Hitler from giving him the most important chair at Heidelberg University. So he had gone into hiding on hearing of the Americans' approach, fearing that he might be shot. But after a fortnight of wandering from one hideout to another, the tired old man had decided to give himself up.

'What shall we do with him?' asked the officer.

Goudsmit was recalling what he knew of Lenard's history. 'Nothing,' he replied. 'We'll just ignore him. He's so vain, that will be the worst punishment for him.'

But there were other 'important brains' in Heidelberg that Goudsmit had no thought of ignoring. One of the first laboratories that the *Alsos* team occupied was that of Walther Bothe, the German specialist in experimental nuclear physics. Here again, Goudsmit realized the personal ironies of his difficult task. He wrote later:

> As I made my way to the laboratory to see Bothe, I was aware that I did not quite know how to proceed. Here I was going to meet the first enemy scientist who knew me personally, a physicist who belonged to the inner circle of the German uranium project. It had not been too difficult to act authoritatively toward strangers, especially when I was backed up by a couple of real officers. But how could I be authoritative with Bothe, who was not only an old acquaintance and colleague, but certainly my superior as a physicist? How did one command an older and respected colleague to turn over his papers?[1]

Bothe greeted Goudsmit warmly, shook hands with him, and the two were soon absorbed in a long scientific conversation. The older scientist showed Goudsmit his laboratory and apparatus and his cyclotron. But when the American began questioning him about the military value of his work, Bothe's attitude changed. He grew sullen and refused to talk about this subject. Pressed by Goudsmit, he declared that he had burned all his secret documents. Goudsmit wondered whether he was telling the truth. If not, what could be done? Arrest Bothe? But Bothe was not a Nazi, simply a loyal German who had sworn secrecy about his work and did not see that his country's defeat absolved him from his oath.

But other, less outstanding scientists – some of whom had belonged to the SS – had no such scruples. They were only too

[1] Goudsmit, *Alsos*, pp. 77-78.

eager to give all the information they could, and wrote volumi-
nous reports in the hope of saving their skins. However, all this
verbiage was of little interest to Goudsmit.

Bothe did not want Goudsmit to think he was hostile to the
Allies; although not prepared to talk about the secret side of his
work, he was quite ready to give information about the organization of nuclear research in Germany. He told Goudsmit that
Otto Hahn had been evacuated to Tailfingen, a small town south
of Stuttgart and not far from Hechingen; and that two well-known
physicists, Heisenberg himself and Max von Laue, were at Hechingen, as was Weiszäcker. They had worked for some years at
the Kaiser Wilhelm Institute in Berlin, had moved for a short
time to Leipzig, and then built an experimental uranium pile at
Berlin-Dahlem. Air-raids had obliged Heisenberg to remove the
uranium pile to Haigerloch, another small town near Hechingen.

Among the scientists captured at Heidelberg were Richard
Kuhn, a brilliant organic chemist, and Wolfgang Gertner, the
man who had made the agreement with Joliot-Curie and worked
with him in Paris. These two also supplied the *Alsos* team with
useful information; and discoveries made in the laboratories recently used by the Germans helped to complete the picture.

It became clear that the German effort in atomic physics had
been conducted by two rival groups that had fiercely competed
for allocations of uranium and research equipment. One group
worked under Heisenberg, the other under Kurt Diebner at
Frankfurt, later at Ilm, in Thuringia. Similar or related work had
been done by a number of other scientists – by Harteck in
Hamburg, Kirchner in Garmisch, Stetter in Vienna, Manfred
von Ardenne in Berlin and Groth in Celle.

The next problem for *Alsos* was to decide where to make a
start.

The Gestapo Looks In

Goudsmit returned to the Paris office for a few days, and while
there he was informed that Ilm had fallen to Patton's Seventh
Army. It was urgent for an *Alsos* team to get there at once. But
how? The place was in Thuringia, deep in the heart of Germany.
Pash was still in Heidelberg, having a well-earned rest after putting two more feathers in his cap – the capture at Nordheim of

Professor Osenberg, chief of planning in the German National Research Council, and the discovery of documents indicating the places to which the various scientific institutes had been evacuated. Goudsmit decided to get a message to Pash.

A close friend of Goudsmit, David Griggs, was Civil Affairs Adviser to General Spaatz, and as such had a flying permit. He flew from Paris to Heidelberg and gave the message to Pash, who at once left for Ilm. Then Griggs flew back to Paris, collected Goudsmit and took him to an airfield near Ilm.

This promptness soon brought its rewards. A number of scientists and their families were found living in an old school. The work in the laboratories had obviously been directed towards making a uranium pile. The Americans came across a heap of black briquettes on a patch of ground near the school. 'It's only coal,' said the Germans in chorus. But Pash thought the briquettes were much too heavy for coal. They were in fact blocks of uranium oxide. The whole lot was packed off to the United States, except for a few small, nicely shaped ones which were deemed suitable as paperweights for the *Alsos* office in Paris.

One scientist was missing from those found at Ilm – and he was the 'main objective'. Two days before the town fell to the Americans, the Gestapo had loaded all the important laboratory equipment on lorries and then left, taking the chief scientist, Kurt Diebner, with them. When Diebner's colleagues had wanted to know the destination, the Gestapo men had told them it was secret. However, the scientists thought their director and the equipment had been taken to the 'Bavarian redoubt' where Hitler was preparing to make a last stand.

Another missing scientist was Walter Gerlach, who had the overall responsibility for research in nuclear physics and was the coordinator of the work being done by the various groups. He had left Ilm by his own means a few days before Diebner's departure, also for an unknown destination.

All these disappearances were a matter for anxiety. The Nazis appeared to be intent to the last on producing a nuclear weapon – perhaps they were making a desperate effort somewhere in Bavaria, using the leading lights of their nuclear physicists to put the finishing touches to an A-bomb.

Goudsmit and Pash had their thoughts cut short by news that the French were advancing rapidly in the direction of Hechingen.

General Eisenhower had approved Operation Harborage, but there was no time to lose. Pash, as usual, seized the initiative. . . .

Colonel Pash up to His Old Tricks

French troops guarding the bridge at Horb, some forty miles from Stuttgart, saw a peculiar American convoy approaching them one April morning. It consisted of jeeps, command-cars and armored cars carrying an assortment of American officers, British soldiers, and civilians.

The leading jeep stopped just before the bridge and an American colonel jumped out. He went up to the officer commanding the French detachment and said to him: 'General Devers has requested me to congratulate you on the capture of this bridge. He is very pleased with your success, and is quite certain that you will hold the position as long as required.'

An interpreter translated this little speech into French, while Colonel Pash – for it was no other – returned to his jeep and led the convoy across the bridge.

The French wondered what the Americans were doing in the area. Were they making for Sigmaringen, where Marshal Pétain and other members of the Vichy Government were being held by the Germans? It was essential for the French to be the first to lay hands on their compatriots.

The officer commanding the French detachment sent a despatch-rider after the American convoy, and he was soon back with reassuring news. The Americans had no interest in Sigmaringen, they were making for the Hechingen-Bisingen area. This was confirmed shortly afterwards, when Colonel Pash radioed to the French from his jeep: 'Keep away from the Hechingen area. In a few hours' time it will come under heavy artillery fire.'

Pash had no intention whatever of shelling Hechingen. It held many treasures that he coveted. But his trick gained him time on the French – time he used to advantage by leading an improvised assault on the bastions of German atomic science.

'Don't forget,' General Devers had said to him, 'that while you are having your little war, the rest of us have got to win another, a much bigger one . . .'

Pash had not forgotten. But when he had heard that Operation Harborage would not take place for a week or two, and that the

French were advancing faster than expected, he decided to take action.

His original plan had been to make a parachute drop and seize control of Hechingen long enough to capture the scientists there, and also the documents, then withdraw towards the American lines with his prisoners. This kind of operation appealed to Pash, but Goudsmit had reasoned with him, saying that as the German scientists were not thought to have made much progress towards making an A-bomb, their work at Hechingen was not worth even one Allied soldier twisting his ankle.

Pash listened to the voice of reason and turned to more conventional methods for attaining his objectives. 'I don't think Colonel Pash has ever forgiven me,' Goudsmit said after the war. 'There's no denying that the operation would have been the most dashing of his military career.'

Instead, Pash turned to Brigadier General Harrison, G.2 of the American Sixth Army Group, who gave him operational control of the 1279th Engineer Combat Battalion. So persuasive was Pash that Harrison added all the vehicles he asked for, and even proposed taking part in the operation himself.

The advance of this force was like a drive in the country. Whenever an area was reached which had not already fallen to the Allies, Pash stopped his jeep and telephoned to the burgomaster of the next village, demanding his surrender. Obediently, the small towns and villages capitulated one after the other, by telephone.

On 23 April Pash made a triumphal entry into Haigerloch. On the 24th, after a short fight during the night, the men with a white alpha were in control of Hechingen. On the following day, the brilliant offensive action of the scientist-hunters was completed by the capture of Tailfingen.

The operation had to be given a code-name, of course; and Pash had decided on Humbug. The 'humbugs' set up their headquarters in Hechingen and promptly began securing the laboratories and arresting the scientists before the French arrived on the scene. However, when some French Moroccan troops reached the area they showed no curiosity about the peculiar activities of the Americans. As Goudsmit said: 'The French were much more interested in pigs and chickens than in atomic specialists.'

The German scientists made no resistance. In fact several of

them seemed relieved that their weeks of tension and anxiety had
ended at last.

'Our situation was not very good under Hitler,' said
Weiszäcker, who had been captured at the address given to *Alsos*.
'Then the fighting reached the town, and for twelve hours it kept
changing hands. There were soldiers everywhere, and we wondered what was going to happen to us. Suddenly we saw a detachment coming our way. They were men who knew what they were
after, led by scientists who were known to us. They proved to
be polite but firm.'

'Here Are the Documents!'

Having arrested Weiszäcker, Wirtz and other physicists, the
Alsos team moved on to Tailfingen, where Otto Hahn and Max
von Laue, a former Nobel prize-winner, were believed to be
working. The capture of Hahn was a simple and most courteous
affair. A German in the street pointed out the old school building which contained the chemistry laboratory. Two of the *Alsos*
scientific officers, both chemical engineers, went in and asked to
see Dr Hahn. They were politely taken to his laboratory, where
Hahn rose to greet them; then he asked them to be seated, and
they began their interrogation. 'It was just like a business call,'
said Fred Wardenburg, one of the '*Alsos*' men.

The crucial question was soon put to Hahn: 'Where are the
documents?' All the other captured scientists had claimed that
they had destroyed their secret reports and documents. But Hahn
was too honest to tell a lie. 'Here they are,' he said, producing
them at once. Wardenburg could not get over it. When he asked
the distinguished scientist to accompany him, Hahn agreed without demur. There was only one discordant note to this almost
pleasant meeting – the guard of American soldiers which took
charge of the small group of scientists when they left the building. But the *Alsos* team could not afford to take the slightest risk.

Hahn, Von Laue and their assistants, Weiszäcker and Wirtz
were all in American hands – but where was Heisenberg, the
number-one objective? His office was empty, and his colleagues
had said, when questioned, that he had gone off on a bicycle at
three in the morning, some days previously, probably to join his
family in Upper Bavaria.

His family – or Hitler's redoubt in the Bavarian Alps?

At any rate, Pash had a shock when he entered Heisenberg's office in Hechingen. He was with General Harrison, and the first thing that met their eyes was a photograph of Heisenberg and Goudsmit together!

Goudsmit has described the incident:

> The photograph had been taken when Heisenberg was my guest at Michigan in 1939. Egged on by Colonel Pash, the General almost began to believe that I could not be trusted and that I had close contact with the enemy.[2]

Naturally, Goudsmit could have explained this without any difficulty. But he thought that this was hardly the moment to try to tell a professional army officer just what the great international brotherhood of physicists had been like before the war.

With Heisenberg still free, it could not be said that the notorious atomic secrets of the Third Reich had all been discovered. However, this was not for lack of trying on the part of *Alsos*. One team found the 'textile factory' which had been mentioned in a report from Switzerland; it had been completely converted into a research establishment, with offices and laboratories. In an abandoned brewery the Americans came across a room papered with strips of silver. It had contained the uranium pile which had been moved from Berlin to Hechingen; despite all the reports, the pile was actually no more than experimental and was not self-sustaining. At Haigerloch, *Alsos* men found a tunnel hollowed out of a cliff which led them to Ali Baba's cave itself – a storeroom which had been enlarged in preparation for a second pile.

These discoveries were all to the good, but the heads of the Manhattan Project were justifiably disappointed. For months past, they had shuddered and had held anxious discussions at the mere mention of Hechingen. For weeks, the *Alsos* members had been excited at the prospect of discovering awful secrets and thereby saving the world from a horrible nightmare; and now the spectre of the German atom-bomb was fast receding. Goudsmit was the only one who had seen matters clearly; he had always said that the German scientists were far short of a finished atom-bomb, although if the war lasted another two or three years ...

[2] Goudsmit, *Alsos*, p. 99.

He later summed up Operation Humbug: 'We wondered whether our government had not allocated more money to its Research Services than the Germans had given for the whole of their scientific work. Compared with ours, the German laboratories were no more than playthings.'

Heisenberg, before disappearing, had given his colleagues and assistants strict instructions that these stocks of uranium oxide and heavy water must on no account fall into the hands of the enemy. However, he had overlooked the fact that his colleagues, once in enemy hands themselves, despondent and defeated, would be prepared to seek a *modus vivendi* with the victors, and that some who had been pro-Nazis would hasten to ingratiate themselves by revealing any secret they knew. As a result of such a disclosure, an *Alsos* team broke into a barn near Haigerloch and emerged triumphantly dragging a handcart laden with blocks of uranium oxide that were still covered with hay. Similarly, a stock of heavy water was discovered in an old mill, and some metallic uranium cubes were dug up from a field outside the town.

The records and documents relating to German research were still missing. But just as *Alsos* prepared to abandon the quest and leave Hechingen on 27 April, Weiszäcker blurted out a few words which gave a lead. Some *Alsos* men went to his house, and in the cesspool at the back found a sealed metal drum containing the records.

That same day, the most incongruous-looking group of prisoners of the Second World War left Hechingen. The masterminds of German atomic science got into jeeps marked with a white alpha, feeling uneasy about their future and the fate of their families. The previous evening an impassive American officer had told them to get ready to leave. Where were they being taken? To a place for further questioning. Was it necessary for them all to go? Could they not send a delegation? No. How long would they be kept? A fortnight at least.

'If they tell us a fortnight,' Wirtz had remarked, 'it means we'll be away for a year at least.'

He did not realize how near the truth he was.

Goudsmit sadly watched them leave. They were six – Otto Hahn, Max von Laue, Carl-Friedrich von Weiszäcker, Erich Bagge, Karl Wirtz and Horst Korsching. What was to become of them? Not so long ago they had been respected scientists, admired for their work even by the enemy; and now they were no more than pitiful prizes of war. They had been hunted down like animals, with machine-guns and armored cars. It was not as though they had been capable of giving Hitler an atom-bomb. Among all the captured documents there would be found copies of letters in which Heisenberg and Weizäcker drew the attention of the German authorities to the possibility of making nuclear weapons, but little progress had been made to that end. The German scientists had not even reached the point where a moral problem might have arisen for them. They had not had to make a choice between helping Hitler to deal out death and refusing to work for him. Were these scientists going to be treated as common prisoners? Would they be put in a prison camp? Their four colleagues captured at Strasbourg were now being held somewhere in the United States. Where would these six end up? Goudsmit wondered. The war had already cost science dearly; *it had reduced the great international brotherhood of scientists to nothing.* The jeeps moved off. Goudsmit wrote after the war:

> It was a sad caravan of command cars and jeeps that departed at last for Heidelberg with our six "prisoners". Seeing them off, I could not help thinking of James Thurber's delightfully absurd cartoon titled "The Capture of Three Physics Professors." I felt a little like Thurber's fierce female pointing her gun at the sorry looking, droopy professors. At any rate, I was glad that I had opposed Colonel Pash's plans for an airborne operation against the physicists. That might have out-Thurbered Thurber.[3]

Less than a fortnight after *Alsos* had left the Hechingen area, taking away the scientists, their equipment and documents, Joliot-Curie arrived with a French team. When he found that his American friends had got there first, he made no attempt to hide his fury. It was not the first time he had been tricked. When he had asked to go to London, innumerable difficulties were raised before he received permission. Once there, he realised that this had been done to give Allied Intelligence the excuse to interrogate him thoroughly. Then there had been the episode of the

---

[3] Goudsmit, *Alsos*, p. 106.

stocks of uranium ore in France, which the Americans had seized without a word to the French authorities. And when Joliot-Curie had gone to see Goudsmit, to 'reveal' all he knew of the work done at Strasbourg by the German physicists, Goudsmit had listened with seemingly great interest – although the Americans had already captured those physicists and had seized all their laboratory equipment.

There could be no question of the French scientist's loyalty, but the Americans were far from convinced. Joliot-Curie had been the first scientist to publish a report on atomic chain-reaction, despite Szilard's campaign for a self-imposed silence. And had not Joliot allowed German scientists to use his laboratory during the Occupation? Was he not a Communist? Besides, France was not a member of the Atomic Club, and there was no reason for the results of research work at Los Alamos to be communicated to her. Such was the American line of thought.

The Capture of Heisenberg

German towns, battered by bombing, were falling to the Allies in rapid succession. *Alsos* was gathering up scientists on every side. At Celle, where thousands of displaced person were parading through the streets behind the flags of their countries, crying joyfully at their new-found freedom, an *Alsos* team arrested Wilhelm Groth, the father of the atomic centrifuge, the 'uranium skimmer' of which more would be heard in later years. At Munich, Gerlach was found in the laboratories of the university. Diebner was picked up twenty miles away, in Schöngeising. Meanwhile Major Lansdale entered Hamburg with the forward British troops and captured Harteck, another specialist in isotope separation. And Dallenberg, a pro-Nazi atomist of Swiss origin, was arrested at his laboratory in Wurtemberg.

All these scientists, and others besides, were taken to *Alsos* headquarters in Heidelberg. There they were sorted out and their fate was decided.

Heidelberg was the beginning of a long and sometimes humiliating odyssey for the most important of them, notably the six from Hechingen. On 1 May they were moved to Rheims in three cars. All they remembered of the town, before they were sent on to Versailles, was the imposing cathedral and the Stens constantly pointing at them. Even more disagreeable was their reception at Versailles. They were thrown into prison with war criminals, and put in cells without tables or chairs. They had ample time to reflect bitterly on the past and wonder anxiously about the future.

On 9 May they were joined by an eminent scientist indeed, no other than Werner Heisenberg. His capture had been something of a saga.

An icy wind was sweeping the slopes of the Bavarian Alps as a patrol from the 56th Infantry Division pushed its way forward, led by an officer with the white alpha insignia – Colonel Pash. Their objective was a chalet belonging to Heisenberg.

The advance elements of the American Seventh Army were still twenty miles behind, there were many German troops in the area, and it was beginning to snow; but nothing could stop Pash. It had become a matter of personal honor for him to capture Heisenberg. Pash had been told that the capture was of less importance now, since it was known that the Germans were a long way from making an atom-bomb; but this made no difference to him. No sooner had he heard of Heisenberg's mountain chalet near Urfeld, in Upper Bavaria, then he decided to go and see if the scientist had taken refuge there. With two armored cars and four jeeps, he had reached Kochel, a small town south of Munich and the most forward area of the American advance. It was snowing, although the date was 2 May, and the lanes were full of slush. Pash borrowed another ten men and continued towards Urfeld.

He had found the bridges destroyed just beyond Kochel. Leaving his vehicles and taking the small patrol with him, Pash had made for Urfeld across the mountain slopes.

A few hours later, the inhabitants of Urfeld saw their first American soldiers, eleven in all.

There was no point in warning Heisenberg, if he was at his chalet, that the net was closing round him. Two GIs went into the village inn and asked: 'Who are the important people around here?'

'There are two,' said the woman behind the bar. 'Professor Heisenberg and the writer, Colin Ross.'

Colin Ross! The American Nazi, the traitor who had stayed

in Germany and worked for Goebbels' Ministry of Propaganda. He had written a book, published in Germany as *Unser Amerika*, in which he enumerated all that the United States owed to Germany.

Since Ross happened to be in Urfeld, *Alsos* would take care of him too.

Pash sent two men to the house where Ross was said to be living, while he went after the quarry which interested him far more. When he reached the chalet and knocked on the door it was opened by Heisenberg himself. 'Professor Heisenberg,' said Pash without any preliminary, 'I know a few scientists who would very much like to see you and have a word or two with you. As of now, consider yourself a prisoner of the American Army.'

As Pash was crisply making this capture which crowned his career as chief of *Alsos*, he heard gunfire down in the village. He hurried back to find two German soldiers lying dead on the village square and two others seriously wounded. Their unit had tried to pass through the village and had come under fire from the American patrol.

Pash noticed the two soldiers he had sent to arrest Colin Ross. They were pale and still trembling from what they had seen. They had found the house, knocked several times without reply, and then forced their way in. A horrible sight had met their eyes. Colin Ross, loyal to 'his' Führer to the end, had killed his wife and child, then committed suicide.

The patrol which Pash had borrowed withdrew to rejoin its unit, leaving the *Alsos* chief in control of Urfeld, assisted by only four men, *Alsos* agents. It was not exactly a comforting situation, for there were thousands of German troops in the mountains round the village.

At sundown Pash received an unexpected visitor, a German general who had learned that the place was occupied by Americans. He surrendered his entire division to the surprised *Alsos* chief.

This was flattering – a division surrendering to a force of five men. But suppose the enemy discovered the truth of the situation? 'I'm in command of advanced elements,' Pash said to the German. 'My General will be here with the division in the morning, and you can formally surrender to him then.'

A little later, another German commander arrived to surrender, and the procedure was repeated. Pash was becoming alarmed about spending the night in such circumstances; and when a third German commander called to surrender, and was told the same tale, Pash decided to withdraw during the night toward the American lines. Before doing so, he went to see Heisenberg at his chalet, left him some food and told him to open the door to no one until he, Pash, returned in the morning. During the night, Pash obtained the support of an infantry battalion, with which he made a second entry into Urfeld. Heisenberg was waiting for him at the chalet, with his bag packed.

The mission of *Alsos* in Germany could be considered completed. The last of the German scientists, and the most important, was in American hands.

CHAPTER FIVE

The Sad Plight of the German Scientists

Priority for Weapons

The *Alsos* 'sorting cage' at Heidelberg was guarded by imposing Negro GIs. Goudsmit warmly welcomed his old friend Heisenberg: 'Wouldn't you like to come to the United States and work with us?' But Heisenberg was as convinced of the superiority of German science as he was of his own importance, and replied coldly. 'No, I don't want to leave; I'm needed in Germany.' However, after a moment's thought, he added: 'If my American colleagues would like to know the extent of our research on uranium, I should be delighted to show them the results of our work when they come to my laboratory.' Goudsmit wrote later:

> It was sad and ironic listening to him say this, when I was aware how much more we knew about the problem than he did. But I could not tell him about the Allied progress, and so I did not contradict him. I merely thanked him for his offer and left him secure in the belief that his work was ahead of ours.[1]

Heisenberg's offer could hardly be called presumptuous. The determined hunt for him and his colleagues was proof enough of their importance. He knew that all the other members of the *Uran-Verein*, the Uranium Club, had been arrested, and that all their apparatus, equipment and files had been seized.

The Allies had indeed drawn an invaluable amount of information from all this plunder, but not in the way that Heisenberg imagined. On the contrary, the deficiency in overall direction of research work in Germany appeared only too clearly; and the

[1] Goudsmit, *Alsos*, p. 113.

Americans were convinced that therein lay the cause of the Nazis' failure to produce an atom-bomb.

Even before the war, science in Hitler's Germany had suffered a basic setback in the rejection of Einstein's theories as 'Jewish physics'. There was also the government's insistence on research to develop military weapons, such as rockets; and gradually the science faculties were depleted of students. Young scientists turned to other fields of endeavor. In 1929 there had been 4,300 chemistry students; ten years later there were only 2,900. When war was declared, thousands of young, capable technical engineers were mobilized into the armed forces; and it was only after considerable pressure by the 'Peenemünde lobby', and after several wasted years, that the Führer consented to release a few of them.

German science had not been able to enlist the support of industry, and without it another 'Oak Ridge' was not possible.

An even greater handicap was the indifference, not to say mistrust, with which the German military leaders regarded the 'long-haired brains'. A German scientist who saw his old acquaintance Goudsmit arriving on the heels of the American advance forces could not help greeting him with: 'Good heavens! Fancy seeing you here so soon. If only we had had our army's confidence and as much influence in military spheres, then you certainly wouldn't be here now!'

There were, of course, exceptions to the general attitude towards research scientists. The German Navy and Air Force both maintained research centers which were well organized, and the Peenemünde establishment in particular was given every facility. But in the eyes of the German warlords, *any research project which could not produce effective weapons almost at once had no value.* Despite Hitler's conviction that final victory was near, he gave priority only to projects capable of producing weapons ready for military use after an experimental period of a few weeks, or at most a few months. By the time a long-term program was seen to be necessary, it was too late.

Nuclear physics had always been the poor relation in the field of military research. The leading scientists of the *Uran-Verein* had made several efforts to interest the military in their work, but had met with no response. In February, 1942, a number of German generals attended a conference on uranium, at which the lunch was prepared by the research scientists themselves, in the hope of arousing a little more appreciation among the military for the wonders of science. It was a 'scientific lunch' – synthetic fats were used for cooking, and each course had been put in a deep-freeze, then heated up before being served. This futuristic menu may have scared the military chiefs; anyway, most of them refused it.

The atomic scientists were themselves to blame for one of the chief causes of their failure – a lack of unity of purpose. There was constant bickering, jealousy, and no exchange of information between the various groups. No coordination was attempted for several years; Heisenberg, for instance, knew very little of what Diebner was doing. Moreover, nearly all the scientists were on bad terms with Dr Esau, who had over-all responsibility for nuclear research. Relationships improved when Esau was replaced by Gerlach, but it was then too late.

One research group came under the Ministry of Munitions, others were directly under military control. Even the Postal Department had its nuclear physics laboratory, under the pedantic Manfred von Ardenne. When Ohnesorge – the only Minister who really believed that the development of a nuclear weapon was possible – raised the matter at a Cabinet meeting, Hitler said jeeringly: 'You see, gentlemen – while our experts are wracking their brains to find a means of winning the war, our Postmaster General produces the solution ...'

Even when scientists had obtained military aid for some project, they had to resort to petty subterfuge to ensure that the support was not withdrawn. For instance, when a certain admiral visited a physics laboratory to see what contribution it was making to the war effort, a physicist showed him a spectrograph used in separating isotopes and blandly told him: 'This apparatus will enable us to produce iron isotopes so light in weight that warships can be built several hundred tons lighter than at present.' Another scientist, Houtermans, needed nicotine for his research work, and asked the military authorities for an allocation of tobacco on the grounds that he was working on the development of a deadly weapon. This was enough for the army, which soon delivered a ton of tobacco; so that the 'nicotine specialists' were able to smoke as much as they liked throughout the war.

Nevertheless, despite this general lack of cooperation, these restrictions and frustrations, the German physicists had not the slightest doubt of the superiority of German over American science. When they were told that an atomic bomb had been dropped on Japan they were completely stunned. By then, the ten oracles of German atomic science were residing in the peaceful surroundings of Farm Hall, set among the green fields of England and not far from the famous Cavendish laboratories of Cambridge University.

From 'Dustbin' to Manor House

Living conditions at the prison in Versailles, the dirt and the humiliating circumstances – especially the fact that the German scientists were treated like war criminals – fully justified the name, 'The Dustbin', which the Americans had given to the prison. The scientists were most indignant at their treatment. They hoped that the arrival of Heisenberg would draw attention to their plight. But nothing happened. Diebner joined them at the same time as Heisenberg, then came Harteck, and finally Gerlach.

Alsos, however, had not forgotten its prisoners, whatever they might have thought. But the white alpha men had come up against army bureaucracy, and despite repeated efforts, had been unable to obtain better treatment for the German scientists. This was chiefly because of a SHAEF order that prohibited preferential treatment for any German prisoner.

But *Alsos* had, in the past, overcome more stubborn obstacles; and the mission succeeded once again in breaking down resistance. On 11 May the scientists were removed to a villa in the Paris suburb of Le Vésinet. The villa *Argentina* had belonged to some wealthy South Americans, but the plumbing and electricity were in a bad state. The scientists, happy to have got away from 'The Dustbin', occupied themselves with restoring these essential services. In the evenings they read some back numbers of *The Physical Review* or played a South American tango – the only piece of music they could find – on the decrepit piano.

Their stay in Le Vésinet did not last long. The American troops in the area took a dim view of these Germans who appeared to be having a good time; and the local French were even more indignant, accusing the officer-in-charge of harboring Marshal Pétain! In order to counteract this discontent, *Alsos* agents started a rumor in the district – that the villa held some prominent anti-Nazis who were being protected from German attempts to kill them.

Nevertheless, the situation became impossible and on 4 June the scientists were moved again, this time to a large house near Huy in Belgium. But troubles began all over again, for the local commander insisted upon issuing POW rations to the Germans. To occupy themselves, the ten scientists held discussions on problems connected with their work, and each in turn gave a lecture on his researches.

At the beginning of July they were told they were going to be taken to England, to their definite place of internment. On the evening of 3 July they arrived at Farm Hall, an eighteenth century manor house which had been used during the war as a training center for secret agents. It had been hastily prepared for its new guests, but time had been found to install secret microphones and recording apparatus. The first conversation to be overheard must have brought a smile to the face of the British officer on duty.

'I wonder whether there are microphones installed here?' said Diebner.

'Microphones installed?' Heisenberg replied with a laugh. 'No, they're not as cunning as all that. I don't think they know the real Gestapo methods. The English have always been a bit old-fashioned.'

The Kidnapping of Goudsmit

The last episode in the *Alsos* epic occurred on 6 August, 1945. Sam Goudsmit, who had captured so many scientists and had even managed to snare the notorious SS Colonel Sievers, was himself kidnapped.

That August morning he was in Berlin, searching the ruins of Himmler's headquarters for records of scientific work carried out by order of the Gestapo, when a jeep came racing up, screeched to a stop, and an *Alsos* officer jumped out to hurry over to Goudsmit.

'You've got just fifteen minutes to catch a plane to Frankfurt,' panted the officer.

'Why Frankfurt?' said Goudsmit in surprise. 'There's still plenty to be done here.'

'It's an order, and the plane is waiting.'

'Can I at least go and fetch my toothbrush?'

'Out of the question! We've already lost over an hour running after you.'

Goudsmit's protests were in vain. The jeep rushed him through the ruins of Berlin to the Tempelhof aerodrome, where an Air Force plane was waiting, ready to take off.

When it landed at Frankfurt, Goudsmit – whose fury can be imagined – went straight to Intelligence HQ and demanded to know the reason for his sudden recall. But no real explanation was forthcoming. Late that night, however, he heard the news over the radio; and the news concerned one of the most stupendous events ever – an atomic bomb had been dropped over Hiroshima. Goudsmit wrote:

> My military guardian angels in Washington were afraid that the news of the bomb might put our Russian colleagues on my tail. There were no barriers in Berlin between the Russian zone and the American. They feared that the Russians might kidnap me and force me to tell the atomic secrets. This was very flattering but rather foolish. Not even the Russians could force me to tell what I didn't know. And it would take months of bureaucratic wrangling before they knew who I was and where I was and how to approach me.
>
> I returned promptly to Berlin and the only Russian who contacted me was a soldier who wanted to buy my watch. As luck would have it, my watch had stopped that very morning, and so my dream of making an easy two hundred and fifty dollars came to nothing.[2]

'The Americans' Bomb? Just Bluff!'

The German scientists organized their time at Farm Hall much as they had done at Huy, holding scientific discussions and giving lectures, playing tennis and walking about the grounds. Heisenberg played the *Appassionata* on the piano. They listened to the news on the radio, they had the run of the library and were supplied with the daily papers. An *Alsos* officer delivered

[2] Goudsmit, *Alsos*, pp. 131-2

letters from the scientists to their families in Germany and collected the replies. Although they had all these amenities, the Germans were completely isolated and held in secret. Not even Goudsmit knew where they were.

On the evening of 6 August, 1945, the officer-in-charge at Farm Hall, went to Otto Hahn's room just before supper and told him the news of the bombing of Hiroshima. Hahn was completely shattered. He had made the original discovery of nuclear fission, and felt personally responsible for what seemed to him a terrible disaster. At the beginning of the war he had said to some friends: 'If our researches lead to an atom-bomb being put in Hitler's hands, then I shall commit suicide.'

'How many have been killed?' Hahn asked.

'Three hundred thousand Japanese,' replied the major, exaggerating a little.

'But that's horrible!'

To which the officer pointed out that it would save the lives of many thousands of Allied soldiers.

After taking some tranquillizers, Hahn went down to supper and announced the news to his colleagues. For some hours he remained so depressed that it was feared he might attempt to take his life. He found a little consolation in the thought that the bomb would probably mean a quick end to the war.

The other scientists were all stunned at the news, but their reactions were different. At first, some thought it was just bluff. Heisenberg and a few others did not believe that an atomic bomb was possible, and said that the adjective 'atomic' had been given to a new kind of high explosive in order to impress the public. When further details were given in later radio bulletins, Heisenberg suggested that the Americans had dropped a whole uranium pile on Japan. It was not until the following day that it occurred to him that the Americans had perhaps used the pile to obtain a supply of plutonium, and that this had been the component of the bomb.

Long discussions took place during the next few days. Some of the scientists were thankful that fate had not given them the responsibility for such a terrible weapon of destruction. Others, especially the younger ones, did not conceal that they had dreamed of making this bomb, and they asked their elders how it was that Germany had lamentably failed where America had succeeded. Gerlach, who as the over-all head of nuclear research was largely responsible for this failure, bowed his head and said nothing. A bitter truth emerged from all these discussions – the German scientists were unable to formulate how the Americans had built their bomb; they could only speculate.

They did understand, however, the reasons for their internment. Considering the relentless way *Alsos* had pursued them, they ought to have suspected earlier. The nearer the Americans came to making an atom-bomb, the more urgent it was to capture the German scientists; to have been forestalled by them at the very last would have indeed been grievous. But the Germans, blinded as they were by their vanity, had not been able to make this deduction at the time. They could not imagine another nation being ahead of them, the *Herrenvolk*, in scientific development.

Now that the secret was out, they felt certain that they would soon be going home. What could the Americans want with them, since their scientific knowledge was so obviously inferior? And they felt little desire to go and work for the Russians.

It was made clear to them that they were not to live in the Russian zone, nor in the French, and guarantees were laid down to this effect. Laboratory facilities were made available to them in Hamburg and Göttingen; and on 7 January 1946, these men who had been *Alsos* 'objectives' were allowed to return to their defeated country.

A few months previously, on 15 October 1945, *Alsos* had been disbanded. It was no exaggeration to say that the purpose of the mission had been completely fulfilled. A few of the officers and scientists were sent to Japan, forming a miniature *Alsos* whose task was to enquire into the resources and stages of development of Japanese science. Colonel Pash was given a special mission in Tokyo, to maintain contact with the Soviet delegation. As for Sam Goudsmit, he returned to the United States weighed down with cases full of secret documents on German scientific research, and began to write his war memoirs.

His book was published in the United States in 1947. He could not have known then that among his many disclosures in the book was a delayed-action bomb which would cause an explosion in his native Holland some fifteen years later. This was the great scandal which became known as 'the *Cellastic* affair'.

CHAPTER SIX

The Cellastic Affair

A Real Jigsaw Puzzle

The long glass-enclosed pleasure boats which ply the grey-green waters of the Amsterdam canals usually slow down as they draw near the famous Heerengracht, and tourists aim their cine-cameras at the historic buildings reflected in the canal. One of these is an impressive red-brick house with white pillars, which the guide-books describe as a blend of Dutch and Italian Renaissance. On the façade, among the statues and bas-reliefs, can be seen the motto of the first occupant of the house, an Italian named Bartolotti: *Ingenio et Assiduo Labore; Religione et Probitate.* Inside, marble corridors lead to vast rooms hung with tapestries and paintings, and containing seventeenth-century furniture.

It is difficult to imagine this historic building, only a few steps from the Royal Palace, as being the center of a scientific spy-ring. The present occupiers are not even aware that it was once the offices of the *Cellastic* company.

When the Cellastic affair broke in 1960 it caused an uproar in Holland. The Communist press roundly accused eminent scientists of having collaborated with the enemy. Other news-papers followed up the story, and questions were raised in the Dutch Parliament. There were street demonstrations, clashes be-tween students and the police, and walls were daubed with in-sulting remarks. Incriminating photos were published, and it was asserted that secret files had been removed from the official arch-ives. A senior Dutch civil servant has said: 'The years 1960–61 will always be known in our country's history as the *Cellastic* period.'

The cause of this great scandal which tore Holland apart can be traced to Sam Goudsmit, as already mentioned. Some revelations in his book unwittingly provided the spark which later set the country ablaze . . .

In the early days of *Alsos* activities in Paris, some sketches of what seemed to be a radar model had been found among a heap of German papers, and had set the mission's bloodhounds on the track of a French engineer. He was found without much difficulty, and was questioned. Over dinner, at which much wine flowed, he made an astounding admission. 'I see you're members of a scientific spy organization,' he said. 'Do you know that during the Occupation the Germans had a similar set-up, here in Paris? I know, because I worked for it. All I had to do was to keep the Germans informed of all the latest inventions and the names of the inventors. They'd given their organization an odd sort of name – *Cellastic*. It must have been the name of a business firm they used as a cover to buy patents in Switzerland and Holland. But my view is that *Cellastic* was nothing more nor less than a German espionage agency.'

The Frenchman obligingly gave the agency's address in Paris – 20, rue Quentin-Bauchart. The *Alsos* men lost no time in going there. It was a large house which belonged to descendants of Marshal Ney, and before the war had been the Venezuelan Embassy. During the Occupation a firm called *Cellastic* had indeed had its offices there.

The Americans made some strange discoveries in the house. There was a chemical laboratory on the first floor, and on the second was a large library of books on pure and applied science. A few rooms had been sound-proofed. But what most intrigued the *Alsos* agents was the curious internal telephone system. They found later that it was one which could not be tapped.

Further searching produced some interesting leads. The letter-box yielded up several messages which the departing Germans had not had time to collect. A list of all the office employees was found, also a payroll showing those who had worked for the firm from time to time.

Sam Goudsmit noticed some scribblings on a desk diary. They were in Dutch, and noted appointments with several French scientists. He also made out the names of two well-known Dutch scientists, Professor Ketelaar of Amsterdam and Professor De

Haas of Leyden, as well as two Dutch research-workers, Zwartsenberg and Kistemaker.

He wondered what all this could mean.

Attempts were made to track down and question two of the French employees who, to judge by their salaries, must have occupied important positions in *Cellastic*. One of them, a radio technician, turned out to be a member of the PPF (the French pro-Nazi party led by Doriot) and was in prison awaiting trial as a collaborator. The other, the head of the firm's secretariat, had completely vanished. According to her neighbors, who spoke of her with respect, she was an attractive young woman. She had moved around from one address to another, until a Prince Charming in a jeep had whisked her away. And so vanished the one chance of meeting that scientific Mata Hari of whom the *Alsos* leaders had often dreamed!

However, a stroke of luck gave *Alsos* a good lead. A small bookseller in the Place de la Sorbonne, who specialized in scientific works, was boasting to Goudsmit of the number of foreign scientists among his customers. He mentioned the Dutch, and said that he had just received a letter from a Monsieur Zwartsenberg, such a nice man, who used to work for a firm in the rue Quentin-Bauchart and was now living with relatives at Pont Saint Pierre near Rouen.

The very next day, Goudsmit and some members of the local FFI were knocking at the door of a Normandy cottage. It was opened by a young man, Zwartsenberg himself.

He refused at first to give any information about *Cellastic*. 'I always thought there was something phoney about the firm,' he admitted. 'But I didn't get mixed up in anything, and I don't want other people who are as innocent as I am to be brought into it.'

This attitude infuriated Goudsmit. He sent the FFI men away, and when he was alone with Zwartsenberg he told him, speaking in Dutch, just how despicable he considered those of his compatriots who had collaborated with the Nazis.

On the following day Zwartsenberg was sumomned to Paris by the Dutch military attaché. There, he proved to be more amenable and told all he knew about the activities of *Cellastic*. Meanwhile, *Alsos* had been following up another lead. A young woman physicist of Rumanian origin, whose name had been on a list of telephone numbers found at the *Cellastic* offices, spoke freely about the nature of her connection with the firm. All she did was to telephone to rue Quentin-Bauchart whenever a lecture was to be given at the Sorbonne by a French or foreign scientist. *Cellastic* paid her well for this information – which was available to anyone who cared to study the notices of forthcoming lectures at the university. The young Rumanian had no idea why *Cellastic* needed this information.

The manager of the Paris office seemed to have stepped straight out of the pages of a spy story. He was an elderly, sick man, highly cultured and an art lover, and owned a very fine collection of pictures and sculpture. He said he was Swiss, but he had a most unusual passport, issued by the principality of Liechtenstein. The name of this mysterious, wealthy man was Ruschewej. He spent nearly all his time at the office, and towards the end had even lived there.

Whether or not he was a spy, he certainly made a good screen for the real brains of the organization. One of these was a Dr Criegee, a chemical scientist by profession. *Alsos* later picked him up in Germany, and he admitted that he had been sent to the Paris office of *Cellastic* in his capacity of Abwehr agent (the Abwehr was the German secret service headed by Admiral Canaris).

Cellastic was run by a South African who had become a naturalized Dutchman. Kleiter, as he called himself, had his headquarters in Holland but often went to Paris. Early in the war he moved the head offices of the company from the Renaissance house in Amsterdam to his own home in a picturesque street in The Hague.

After the liberation of Holland the *Cellastic* case was taken over by the Dutch. Their investigations lasted a long time, but eventually the pieces of the jigsaw puzzle were assembled and the full picture of the *Cellastic* organization became clear ...

Some Very Simple-minded Dutchmen

For Professor Ketelaar it had all begun when he read an advertisement in a Dutch newspaper in January, 1942. A scientific research-worker was required by a Dutch firm. Ketelaar thought a friend of his might be interested, and wrote for details to the address given in the advertisement. A few days later a burly, square-shouldered, typical Dutch business-man called to see him. The visitor gave his name as Kleiter and said in effect: 'After the war we intend to specialize in exploiting patents of products in great demand. To that end, we are making a preliminary study of all the likely inventions which appear in Holland, France and other European countries. Would you be interested in assisting us from time to time?'

Ketelaar had heard of this *Cellastic* company which Kleiter said he represented. It made rubber-bands, and had been started in 1939 by the merger of two firms which bought the rights of foreign patents. The company seemed perfectly respectable to the young professor, and the offer of working for it was made all the more attractive by the prospect of several trips to Paris. So he accepted, and also got his friend Zwartsenberg, who had been a fellow-student, taken on by the company.

Kleiter had also approached a well-known Dutch physicist, Professor De Haas, the director of the *Kammerlingh Omnes* laboratories at Leyden, who was also pleased to accept the offer. De Haas introduced Kleiter to Dr Kistemaker, a brilliant young physicist of Leyden University; he too joined the staff of the company. 'It's a stroke of luck for you,' the two professors told the young men, Zwartsenberg and Kistemaker. 'By working for *Cellastic* you'll avoid being sent to Germany for forced labor.'

Not only did they avoid that unpleasantness, they obtained advantages which included travel to France – and travelling freely was a rare experience for young men in German-occupied countries. The two soon developed the habit of travelling between Amsterdam and Paris as often as possible.

When Goudsmit met Professor Ketelaar towards the end of the war, he said to him: 'In you and De Haas, the Germans succeeded in getting hold of the two most simple-minded scientists in the whole of Holland.' And indeed, neither of them had for a moment suspected that Kleiter was a Nazi. He had settled in Holland long before the war and become a naturalized Dutchman, so that in due course he would be well placed for running his scientific espionage service. The Abwehr had given him its blessing to set up business in Paris, and Dr Criegee had been one of the liaison agents.

However, the two professors could hardly be blamed for not

suspecting anything, in the early days at least. The two younger Dutchmen were indeed spending their time in Paris enquiring into new inventions, and they themselves were employed from time to time in examining inventions that were either quite harm-less – a new kind of soap, for instance – or somewhat eccentric, such as a method of maturing whisky in a very short time. They maintained close and friendly contact with French scientists, Joliot-Curie in particular.

They began to be a little suspicious, nevertheless, as time went on. Ketelaar was the first to remark how easily permits and visas were obtained for him. All he had to do was to hand in his pass-port, and it was soon returned with the necessary stamps and signatures. Then there was the unusual telephone system in the *Cellastic* offices. But when Ketelaar, in his simple way, asked one of the heads of the firm about these telephones, he was given a quite satisfactory reply: the house had been the Venezuelan Em-bassy, and those Latin American countries, with their constant revolutions . . .

Now and again, when Ketelaar thought of going from Amster-dam to Paris, he was told: 'Not just now, our contact man isn't there.' On one occasion when he was at the *Cellastic* offices – where the permanent staff never exceeded twenty-five – he met a scientific chemist who was almost certainly a German but who claimed to be Swiss, and made matters more mysterious by hand-ing round American cigarettes which he said he had got in Zurich, where he had been to see his family.

There were never any callers in uniform at the Paris offices of *Cellastic*, but on the other hand the hotels where the Dutch scientists stayed were full of German officers. Joliot-Curie recalled a visit he had from De Haas one evening. Their discussion on nuclear research had gone on until a late hour, and Joliot-Curie proposed accompanying his visitor back to his hotel. De Haas firmly refused the offer, so Joliot went just a little way with him, to the corner of the street. After they had parted, Joliot looked back and was greatly surprised to see De Haas getting into a German army car, which had obviously been waiting for him.

Did De Haas eventually realize what was the true role of the *Cellastic* set-up? Or had he become unhappy about his work, or balked at his instructions to keep in close touch with French scientists? In any case, taking advantage of the ease of movement which had been given him, he fled to Switzerland with his wife, and from there reached London. However, he never said a word about his Paris activities; and he continued to keep silent about them when he returned to Amsterdam at the end of the war. It was only after the Dutch authorities had received the *Alsos* report on *Cellastic,* and questioned De Haas, that he told his story.

His patriotism was not in doubt. Before the war the Dutch Government had bought a large stock of uranium oxide, on his suggestion, in order to carry out nuclear research. When Holland was invaded, this stock had been hidden; and although De Haas knew where it was, he had never given any indication to the Germans. The possession of this uranium oxide later enabled Holland to conclude a joint research program with Norway and so obtain supplies of heavy water – the only country, apart from the major powers, to do so.

But if De Haas was not pro-Nazi, why had he said nothing about *Cellastic* when he reached London? Perhaps it was from fear, or – as Goudsmit suggested – because he was so simple?

In any case, he and Ketelaar had been putty in the hands of the Nazis. The Germans' object had been to assure themselves that scientists of occupied countries were not working on projects which could be detrimental to Germany, and to be kept informed as to whether any research work might aid the German war effort, and if so, to direct it into channels where it could serve military purposes. The Germans fully realized that they could not achieve this themselves; scientists of the occupied countries were too hostile to them to accept direct interference. So the only way of being present in their laboratories was through a third party, through Dutch or Swiss scientists who would be accepted as colleagues to whom the scientists could talk freely.

Such was the role of the Paris branch of *Cellastic,* and neither the scientists doing the spying nor the scientists spied upon ever seemed to have fully realized it.

The Scandal Breaks

Soon after the war, the Dutch authorities ended their enquiries into the *Cellastic* case. Kistemaker and Zwartsenberg were questioned about the part they had played, but the matter was pursued no further when they proved that they had acted upon the advice of their professors. Ketelaar and De Haas were suspended, but were allowed to return to academic life after the enquiry had reported that, despite their thoughtlessness, they had not contributed to the enemy war effort. The case was officially closed, and the whole business seemed to have been forgotten. But fifteen years later the name of Dr Kistemaker was spread across the front page of the Dutch Communist paper *Waarheid*.

It must be said that the young scientist had had an extraordinary career since 1945, having become one of Europe's leading atomic specialists. No one remembered his past connection with the *Cellastic* case, until he happened to make what can only be called a rash decision. He engaged in a joint research project with some German scientists, one of whom was Wilhelm Groth, 'the father of the centrifuge', who was producing uranium cheaply for a large industrial concern, Degussa, at Bonn. The head of Degussa was none other than Dr Alfred Richard Boettcher, the man who, under the protection of the SS, had plundered the University of Leyden of much of its physics equipment during the war. This laboratory equipment had been taken to Doetinchen, a small town on the Dutch-German frontier, where the Nazis had set up a 'purely German' physics institute. When the town was threatened by the Allied advance, the Germans had evacuated all the equipment stolen from Leyden.

A chemistry worker in Professor Ketelaar's laboratory who had been refused promotion happened to read Goudsmit's book, and thought he had found a means of getting his own back. He showed the Communists the passages relating to the *Cellastic* case, in which the Dutch scientists were mentioned though their names were not given. However, the Communist papers had little trouble in working up a campaign whereby Kistemaker was accused of collusion with the ex-Nazi who had plundered Leyden University. This, in a country which still remembered the horrors of Nazi perpetrations, was quite sufficient to stir up an enormous scandal.

Waarheid led a crusade against 'the warmongers', organized demonstrations at universities and provoked clashes between Left-wing students and the police. Klaus Fuchs was quoted from East Germany as saying that Kistemaker was working with German scientists in the West to produce an H-bomb. One morning,

Kistemaker found the front of his house had been daubed with swastikas and the words 'Kistemaker-A-bomb maker'.

The Communist press kept up the campaign, daily introducing fresh accusations, attacking Ketelaar and even his wife; and other newspapers joined in the dispute. The Shell Company, for whom Dr Zwarstenberg had been working for some years, suddenly dismissed him without notice. Questions were asked in Parliament, and twice the Minister for Education had to clear Kistemaker and to prove that the Government had not destroyed the files concerning the scientist's wartime activities.

The storm continued to rumble throughout 1960 and well into 1961, and when it finally died away it left the chief victims deeply affected in their private and professional lives. Their association with *Cellastic* had enabled them, during the war, to make pleasant trips to Paris and to have a good time while their compatriots were suffering under the Nazi yoke, but they could not have thought they would pay heavily for it all some fifteen years later.

CHAPTER SEVEN

The Wonder Weapons

'Stalin Organs'

Cellastic ... Alsos ... The existence of such an organization in each camp was in itself a sign of anxiety, of a dull fear which had gripped the all-powerful chiefs of the secret services. Who knew whether some scientist or other was not about to produce the wonder weapon which, against all logic, could suddenly bring victory to an enemy at his last gasp? An atomic bomb in the hands of the Nazis, or a hail of devastating rockets on New York, would have profoundly changed the course of the war even when Germany was near collapse. Hitler realized this in 1943 and gave priority to a complete conversion of German heavy industry with a view to producing a flow of *Wunder Waffen,* wonder weapons. As the war spread to all parts of the globe, the secret service chiefs on both sides had realized the great importance of the scientific research being conducted in enemy laboratories. And audacious attempts were made, often at the cost of many lives, to destroy or capture a new weapon or scientific aid of great potential while it was still in a stage of development.

In 1941 the Russians had deployed their *Katioushas,* small rockets loaded with shrapnel and explosive which were fired from 'Stalin Organs' in salvoes of thirty at a time. These *Katioushas* not only were deadly, but made a thunderous noise and hurtled through the air in a sheet of flame. They shattered the morale of the Wehrmacht.

In order to find a reply to this latest enemy invention, the Germans mounted what can only be called a desperation effort. They employed secret agents, paratroops and reconnaissance planes in an endeavor to seize one of the inventors of the rockets, a scientist named Leontiev, and to capture one of the 'Stalin organs'. But the operation was a total failure; and the *Katioushas* continued to spread fear and destruction in the ranks of the German army.

Another operation with a comparable aim, mounted by the Scientific Section of British Intelligence and given the code-name Eldorado, met with complete success.

The British were greatly worried by the fact that their bombers over Berlin were being shot down with such precision that it seemed obvious the anti-aircraft batteries had been equipped with a new form of radar. A diabolically clever plan was evolved. The German naval base at Brest, in France, was bombed night after night, and – as had been hoped – the Germans sent one of their latest anti-aircraft batteries from Berlin, complete with its radar equipment. Whereupon, on 27 April 1942, a small commando unit entered Brest harbor in rubber dinghies, while a RAF raid was taking place, and seized the important parts of the battery's radar equipment. These were successfully taken back to England, and enabled scientists to produce a jamming apparatus which was soon fitted in all RAF bombers.

This kind of hazardous operations sometimes took place much farther afield. The American secret service, for instance, sent an agent into Hungary to rescue an Hungarian scientist from the clutches of the Germans. The scientist, who had been working with Professor Oberth, had succeeded in escaping from Germany and was being sheltered by the Resistance in a village deep in the heart of Hungary. When the Americans heard of this they mounted a rescue operation. In January, 1944, the agent parachuted into Yugoslavia and made his way towards Hungary. One dark night, three months later, an American submarine surfaced off an Adriatic beach and took off the waiting agent and the scientist. They were landed at Bari, and from there the scientist was taken to the United States, eventually to become one of the pioneers in guided missiles.

However, when this scientist first arrived in the United States, he found there was a great interest in rockets of the most curious, not to say fantastic, kind. The Japanese secret service had got wind of them too, and was anxiously wondering what truth there was behind the rumors of the 'living rockets' invented by Professor Adams.

The 'Living Rockets'

Adams, an unassuming research-worker well into middle age, had been thoroughly roused by the Japanese attack on Pearl Harbor. A short time afterwards he called at the Pentagon to tell of his invention which would spread fire and disaster across Japan. The officers who received him listened at first with amused disbelief, as well they might, but nevertheless gave him their attention.

In Japan, said Professor Adams, the towns are built chiefly of wood, so small incendiary bombs placed in the roofs would easily set the whole place on fire. True – but who was going to place the incendiaries? Living rockets, Adams replied. The officers looked at each other with a knowing little smile, which spread to a broad grin when Adams went on to explain what he meant by 'living rockets' – simply bats, hundreds of thousands of bats. Adams, taking no notice of the officers' reaction, continued to elaborate his idea. Bats are capable of carrying three times their own weight; they hide in roofs, where they usually get rid of anything attached to their bodies. If a dozen bombers were to be loaded with bats, all dormant and carrying small incendiaries carefully set, and if the bats were released over Japan, the sun would wake them up, they would go and hide away in roofs and their little burdens would soon start up innumerable fires.

While the elderly professor was talking, the amused disbelief of the officers had changed to enthusiastic support for his idea. A decision was made at once to hold a conference on the subject. The result was that a credit of two million dollars was allocated for the project, and the army promised the professor all the help he needed.

Army scientists began work on making tiny napalm bombs for the bats to carry tied round their bodies. Hundreds of soldiers and civilians went hunting for a Mexican species of bat which seemed the most suitable for the suicide-mission. Detailed experiments were carried out to ensure that the transport and dropping of these unsuspecting heroes would be effected in the best possible way. In the course of a demonstration in the Texan desert a thousand bats set fire to many thousand wooden crates. The next demonstration was expected to be an even greater success, and so it was; yet it put an end to Professor Adams's hopes.

One summer evening in 1942 several senior officers gathered at the Carlsbad air-base in Texas for a sensational demonstration. Scientists showed them half a dozen bats in a state of hibernation; each had a belt of tiny napalm bombs slung round its body. In the morning they were to be dropped from aircraft over buildings erected out in the desert. Unfortunately, the scientists had overlooked the fact that the sun gets quite hot very early in the morning at that time of year. The bats were awake before the generals were out of bed, and flew about in all directions, setting fire to hangars and office buildings. Soon, much of the air-base was ablaze. Adams lost all his papers and documents in the fire. The generals were not at all pleased, and a week later Adams received a brief letter informing him that the army was no longer interested in his living rockets.

The Japanese secret service, which had been keeping an interested eye on the progress of the scheme, was able to breathe afresh. It seemed odd, nevertheless, that the Americans should give up a project which promised good results, simply because a few generals were annoyed at having been present at a fiasco. Not until the A-bomb was dropped over Hiroshima did the Japanese realize that the American High Command had not acted through vexation. There was no need of 'living rockets' when the death bomb was being developed. The Manhattan Project allowed the bats to be returned to their peacetime occupations.

A Flood of Rumors

The bats could be returned, but not the scientists. They were being kept busy by the war leaders. One question was constantly put to them, in Russia, Britain and the United States alike: 'Can you produce a wonder weapon?' And this question concealed another, one that was haunting the Allied Commands – will Germany discover a wonder weapon before we do?

German science, because of its great prestige and backing from propaganda, seemed to have some very unpleasant surprises in store. Its leading lights had split the atom, made rocket missiles and produced aero-engines of unsurpassed power. Who knew what they were making in their underground laboratories and factories?

Stories put out from Zurich or Stockholm, and picked up by the British and American press, gave indications of some fantastic German schemes. There were to be tons of liquid air sent over the English Channel, making icebergs which would block British ports; clouds of ice-crystals would prevent British bombers from taking off. The mysterious constructions which appeared on the French coast were said to be containers for the 'Red death' which could destroy London, or for poison gas which could destroy all life in Britain. The thick, black, 400-feet-long pipes, stretching across the French beaches like steely serpents, could be a new type of gun with an acceleration system which would fire shells loaded with a special explosive right into the heart of London. These 'guns' preoccupied pessimists for many months, until after D-Day.

The chiefs of the British secret services, however, had worries which seemed much more serious. A young woman officer whose job in the WRAF was to examine reconnaissance photographs noticed a strange T-shaped object on one reel taken over Germany. This minute 'T' set off one of the biggest scientific battles of the war. And it earned Miss Constance Babbington Smith, the young WRAF officer, the unusual title – but one greatly to her credit – of 'Miss Peenemünde'.

The Riddle of Peenemünde

It was quite by chance that Bernard Newman, a British agent who travelled about Europe as an innocent tourist and wrote excellent travel books, had in 1938 come across some installations built of reinforced concrete and surrounded by barbed-wire on the Baltic coast of Germany, opposite Rügen Island. Some friendly and talkative hotelkeepers had told him that Peenemünde, as the place was named, was used for experiments with new-type rockets. 'What's more,' one of the Germans had added, 'a rocket was launched bearing a criminal who had been sentenced to death!'

At that time, the British secret service had no reason for attaching any particular importance to Peenemünde. Nevertheless, the place was included in the flight plan of a Canadian 'civil' air pilot,

Bob Niven. He always had a passenger with him – Sydney
Cotton, an expert aerial photographer, who had fitted a tiny precision camera in the belly of the aircraft. The two often flew to
Germany and always had a friendly reception from airport officials. However, when they landed at Tempelhof aerodrome on
1 August 1939, and showed the authorities their flight plan –
which included Peenemünde – they were at once taken before a
senior officer. He sharply informed them that civil aircraft were
no longer allowed to fly over Germany, and that they must leave
the country forthwith. Niven and Cotton flew back to England
wondering why the Germans had become so distrustful. A month
later they knew the answer, when the Nazis invaded Poland and
war was declared.

The directors of British Intelligence had other concerns than
the riddle of Peenemünde. But Churchill's son-in-law, Duncan
Sandys, the Minister responsible for the 'special services', was
not inclined to let the matter rest. He happened to meet a young
professor of astrophysics, V.R. Jones, who had been following the
experiments of the German space-explorers for some years. He
had read Von Braun's paper on liquid-fuel rockets. But no news
of further experiments had come out of Germany for some time
before the outbreak of war; no one knew where the scientists interested in rocket research were working or what had become of
them.

When Sandys heard this, sparks flew. Could the German
rocket scientists be hidden away at Peenemünde? A secret agent
must be introduced into the place at all costs!

This was not necessary, because a few days later a top-secret
cable from Norway arrived on Sandys's desk: 'Am sending by
special courier highly important report on Peenemünde. MA-2
Oslo.'

'MA-2' was Rear-Admiral H. Boyes, the naval attaché at the
British Embassy. He had not exaggerated the importance of the
report. It contained technical details, the facts and figures, concerning the rocket missiles and pilotless aircraft that were being
developed in the secret workshops at Peenemünde.

When Professor Jones was shown the report, he was quite sure
– it could have been made only by someone with an advanced
knowledge of astrophysics, a specialist in rocket problems. Who
could it be? At the time, the report was classified as anonymous.

And as such it remains today. But there can be no doubt that the anonymous author of the report is known by name to a few people in the British Secret Service, and that he was already known when the report was first received. One name has been mentioned – an eminent German scientist who specialized in radar and was working at Peenemünde, an ardent anti-Nazi who considered it his duty to warn the Allies of Hitler's secret plans. The British were naturally most grateful to him; and the best way of showing it was *never to reveal his name*, so that he has remained 'the greatest secret of the Second World War'.

The report which could have cost the brave German scientist his life did not lead to any action against Peenemünde. It was filed away, or got buried under what seemed to be more urgent matters; and a long time passed before the alarm was again sounded.

Then it was given by some Poles. Among the thousands of forced laborers whom the Germans commandeered in Poland were three young men who were in close touch with the Resistance. Just before they left for Germany, a caller had said to them: 'When you get to Germany, don't forget to keep your eyes open. If you see anything interesting, send me word by making some reference to Yadwiga. I shall understand, and you can leave the rest to me.'

Towards the end of 1941 the three young Poles were sent to the labor camp at Trassenheide, where thousands of foreign workers at the Peenemünde base were quartered. It did not take the three long to discover that something odd was in progress behind the barbed-wire perimeter. A postcard enquiring after the health of Auntie Yadwiga was sent to Warsaw. A fortnight later, a German officer from the T O D T organization arrived for a 'routine inspection'. While going round the camp he managed to have a word with the three Poles. 'Aunt Yadwiga sent me,' he said in Polish.

Obeying instructions from this agent of the Resistance, the three volunteered for the cleaning gangs; and after a few weeks they were able to make a detailed plan of the Peenemünde installations. This plan reached Stockholm, and from there was sent to London.

Other reports of suspicious activity in the Peenemünde area were reaching London at about this time, originating from foreign workers in Germany, British Intelligence agents and travellers from neutral countries. However, Sandys needed more powerful arguments to convince the Chiefs of Staff that it was time some action was taken. So on 23 June 1943, two Spitfires equipped with the latest photographic apparatus took off to fly over Peenemünde. On their return, the films were given to Constance Babbington Smith ('Babs') for examination.

In a matter of minutes, 'Babs' had laid her claim to the title of 'Miss Peenemünde'. Viewed through the stereoscope, a tiny T-shaped object could be discerned on several of the films, among the buildings and hangars. It was not an aircraft on the ground, nor was it a huge bomb. Just what it was, 'Babs' had no idea. Although she did not then know it, she was the first British person to see a V.1, one of the pilotless flying-bombs which, a year later, were sent on their destructive missions over southeast England.

The still mysterious 'T' object passed rapidly before the eyes of the hierarchy and quickly reached Duncan Sandys. He called in Professor Jones, and the two could not help feeling some satisfaction, despite the awful threat implied in the photographs. That evening, an emergency meeting of the War Cabinet was held, at which the Chiefs of Staff and the Government's scientific advisers were present. Sandys spoke of the Germans' development of rockets as missiles, of the technical advances which had been made, and asked for immediate action against Peenemünde. Delay would place Britain in grave danger.

He did not succeed at first in convincing everyone. Jones and his assistants emphasized the importance to Hitler of a flying-bomb capable of bringing destruction to England. But Churchill's scientific adviser, Professor Lindemann, and all his team expressed some doubts. They referred to 'the Peenemünde hysteria' and feared that it was just another trap set by Goebbels's propaganda machine.

Sandys kept his trump card to the last. He told of the reports on Peenemünde received from various sources, and then spread out the aerial photos with their little white 'T', which was almost certainly one of the flying-bombs ready for a test flight. This convinced Churchill, and orders were at once sent to Bomber Command for an attack on Peenemünde.

Operation Crossbow was launched, and at 0130 hours on 17

August 1943, one of the largest bomber forces ever assembled began to take off from British airfields. There was a full moon as the 608 Lancasters led by Group-Captain Searby, the 'Master Bomber', made for Rügen Island and went in over Peenemünde in thirty-one waves. The bombers were over Peenemünde for 104 minutes and dropped two thousand bombs – fifteen hundred tons of explosives and incendiaries. In spite of the intense ack-ack fire, only forty-one aircraft were lost over the target.

The war had at last been carried to the scientists; London did not disguise the fact that one of the chief targets had been the living quarters of the research-workers and technical staff.

However, the results of the operation were disappointing. Reconnaissance showed that comparatively little damage had been caused to the main installations. The Germans were soon able to resume their experiments and production. The damaged buildings were repaired and the scientists, instead of all living together, were distributed among the holiday hotels along the coast. Most of the 735 people killed in the raid had been foreign workers from the camp at Trassenheide. The dead among the Peenemünde staff numbered 178, but only two or three were important scientists.

Some Curious 'Pairs of Skis'

The bombing attack on the night of 17 August, however, was but the first of Operation Crossbow. During the following weeks, the Allied air forces kept up their attempts to crush the menace of Hitler's wonder weapons. While the first raid on Peenemünde had been taking place, other formations were bombing the Rax works at Vienna and the Demag plant in Western Germany. Ten days later an attack was made on Watten, a place on the French coast where British Intelligence had noted unusual activity.

Huge bunkers of an odd shape were reported recently built at Watten and at seven other places on the coast of the Pas de Calais, as well as at Cherbourg; and British specialists soon concluded that there was a close connection between these bunkers and the secret weapons being perfected at Peenemünde. During September and October the places were bombed many times; the bomber crews were not aware, of course, that the bunkers were intended for the V.2s being produced in secret factories deep inside Germany.

Even greater anxiety was felt by Allied Command when they received reports, towards the end of the summer, of other strange constructions. This time it was two concrete tracks about one hundred yards long; from the air they looked so much like a pair of skis that RAF observers were soon referring to them as 'ski sites'. By mid-November, twenty-one such sites had been discovered. And all of them were pointing towards London. The obvious inference was that they were launching ramps for flying-bombs.

Immediate action was called for, and on a large scale. Allied aircraft flew a great number of reconnaissance missions. Within a week, sixty-four 'pairs of skis' were sighted along the French and Belgian coast. Three weeks later, the number had risen to seventy-five. Just before Christmas a massive air attack was delivered; thirteen hundred bombers dropped their loads on the concrete sites hidden among the dunes. The destruction was great, but the sites were soon rebuilt. At the end of January the total was put at one hundred and fifty.

Washington was worried too – the success of 'Overlord' (the Normandy invasion) might be jeopardized by these flying-bombs. Secretary of State Stimson set up a special committee to study the matter. Some people were already suggesting that the Normandy landings should be abandoned and another area chosen for the opening of the Second Front. Others proposed spraying the 'ski sites' with poison gas, but this was sheer desperation. The only logical solution was still to bomb the sites heavily, and with ever greater precision. And in order to discover the most effective manner of attack, there was the Eglin Field air-base down in Florida. This was a 'scientific' airfield where new types of bombs were tried out, and enemy fortified positions were reproduced so that the Air Force could practice destroying them.

On 25 January 1944, General Marshall was on the line to the base commander, telling him about the 'pairs of skis' and ordering him to have models of them constructed at Eglin Field. 'I want everything to be ready as soon as possible,' said Marshall. 'Top priority!'

Some thousands of civilian workers and army personnel were set to work; building material arrived at the base from all parts of the United States, by rail, road, and sea, and even by air-lift. Exact replicas of the sites along the northern coast of France were built in steel and reinforced concrete; they were then camouflaged, ringed with anti-aircraft guns, and bomber squadrons armed with the latest weapons practiced attacking them. Camera crews from Hollywood took miles of film as the bombers tried to smash the installations to pieces, and this enabled a conclusion to be reached in a very short time – that the best way of attacking the launching sites was by dropping heavy bombs from a low altitude.

Staff officers flew to England to see General Eisenhower; they showed the films to the Air Force chiefs, and obtained the highest priority from the Supreme Commander for the bombing of the launching sites. Thus, right up to D-Day, the concrete 'pairs of skis' were regularly attacked by Allied bombers.

Meanwhile, British Intelligence had been attacking the problem in a different manner. Secret agents, helped by the French Resistance, had kept watch on the movements of a splendid black Chrysler, once the property of the King of the Belgians, which was being used by two Germans of high importance – Colonel Wachtel, the officer commanding the V.1 launching sites, and his scientific adviser, Professor Sommerfeld.

The plan was to kidnap these two and take them to England. One day in the spring of 1944 everything was ready for the attempt. Trusted Resistance members took up positions in certain streets in Amiens; a black Citroen was waiting at a corner, ready to be driven off. As expected Colonel Wachtel was seen leaving the Kommandantur alone. When he had got some distance from it, he was to be seized and bundled into the waiting car. But the colonel was not at all helpful; instead of walking along the street, he merely crossed the roadway and went into the officers' club opposite, a possibility which had not been considered. So the attempt to kidnap Wachtel failed.

When D-Day came, Allied Command found that fears of disruption by V.1s were groundless. The Normandy invasion was successfully under way by the time the first flying-bombs fell on London. Then, on 8 September, the first V.2s came into operation. The hour of Hitler's wonder weapons had arrived.

It was on 12 June 1944, six days after D-Day, that the first four flying-bombs were launched on London. The following day, the words 'rocket missile' were pronounced for the first time in

the House of Commons. All the efforts of secret agents, saboteurs and Allied bombers had not been able to prevent what had
long been dreaded – direct attacks on London by weapons fired
from bases on the Continent. However, means of defense against
the 'doodlebugs' were soon found. Their speed in flight was no
more than 400 m.p.h., and they could be shot down by fighter
aircraft and by ack-ack guns. A technique was developed by bold
RAF fighter-pilots; they flew alongside a V.1, and with a sudden
wing movement created a current of air which caused the flying-
bomb to deviate from its course and to head towards the North
Sea, where it was safely shot down.

The balloon barrage which had proved effective against German
bombers earlier in the war was again put up around London, and
again it proved its worth. When a V.1 flew into one of the trailing
wires it got blown up.

Neither fighter-planes nor balloon barrage, however, could do
anything against the V.2s. These supersonic rockets, with a war-
head containing a ton of high explosive, gave no warning of their
approach; the first that people heard of one was when it broke
through the sound barrier, and by then it had landed and exploded. Houses, cinemas and office buildings were destroyed, but
fortunately each V.2 caused comparatively few casualties. No official mention was made of them for two months, in order to deny
the enemy any information on the results obtained by his new
weapon. Then, on 10 November, Churchill briefly announced in
Parliament that a long-range German rocket had come into operation, and that several had recently fallen in the London area.

Although no defense was possible against the V.2s, the British
had at least one consolation. A complete V.2 rocket in perfect
working order was in their possession.

The Missing V.2

One day in early June the telephone had rung in Walter
Dornberger's office. He had recently been appointed head of the
rocket program. The call was from the Führer's headquarters.
Had a V.2 been launched from Peenemünde in the last few days?
The voice seemed most anxious, and Dornberger quickly had enquiries made. He learned that a V.2 had indeed been launched,
one fitted with the remote-control mechanism of the new anti-

aircraft rocket *Wasserfall*. The launching had been without incident, but then the V.2 had swerved in its trajectory, for no known reason, and had vanished into the clouds. Since then, nothing had been heard of it.

Dornberger informed Hitler's HQ, and in reply was told that news had been received of the missing V.2: it had exploded in the air over Sweden, and what remained of its mechanism had fallen into some marshes near Kalmar. Hitler was furious. He wanted to know whether an examination of the mechanism would reveal the principle of the V.2 and its capabilities. Dornberger, in great distress, was obliged to reply in the affirmative.

Hitler summoned him to Rastenburg, where the Führer's HQ was then situated. Dornberger went expecting a first-class blowing up, but Jodl was there to greet him when he stepped off his plane and at once reassured him. The Führer had come round to thinking that it was no bad thing for Sweden to understand that she could be bombarded from a distance, should the necessity arise.

Whether the Swedish Government did understand the veiled threat or not, it continued to play its neutral game and made no attempt to conceal the fact that the V.2 engine had fallen on its territory. Shortly afterwards, the British Ambassador called on the Swedish Foreign Minister and requested that the rocket be handed over to his country. 'We are at war with Germany, and it is quite certain that the rocket was meant for us,' he said firmly. 'Consequently, it belongs to us, and we should like to have it in the same state as it was found.'

The Swedish Minister opposed the claim, for form's sake, but ended by agreeing to hand over the 'lost object', which was being carefully looked after. But there was one condition – the British had to come and fetch it. London did not have to be asked twice. A Dakota, piloted by an American ace, flew to Stockholm and took off again with the precious 'wonder weapon' on board. The plane had to fly across German-occupied Norway, but this was successfully accomplished in spite of the great weight of the cargo. It landed in England, and the remains of the V.2 were soon being examined by Air Force scientists, who then set to work to construct a copy of the weapon.

The V.1 and the V.2 were proof that German 'wonder weapon' propaganda had not lied. The few British and American experts who examined the body of the weapon brought from Sweden were amazed at its power and perfection. And the Germans were said to be making a V.3! What manner of wonder weapon would that be? An atomic bomb or a death ray? The Allied information services tried to calm the fears of the public. *Time* magazine published an article which demonstrated that never in history had a secret weapon changed the outcome of a war.

While the public were being reassured, Allied air forces increased their bombing of enemy industrial plants, fuel depots and research centers. But the number of rocket missiles falling on England did not decrease. They seemed to shoot up from all over northern France, Belgium and Holland, from 'ski sites', reinforced bunkers and mobile launching ramps. 'I feel certain that if the enemy had succeeded in using these weapons for a period of six months,' Eisenhower later wrote in his *Report by the Supreme Commander*, 'and especially if he had made the Portsmouth-Southampton area one of his chief targets, then Overlord would have had to be called off.'

But those six months were lost to the enemy. The Normandy invasion went ahead as planned and the Allies overran the V.2 launching sites in northern France. The sites in Belgium were hastily abandoned as the British spearhead liberated Brussels and pressed on to free southern Holland. In a last desperate attempt, the Germans launched their missiles on the port of Antwerp, which the Allies had just opened up, from sites in the north of Holland. But this came too late to have any effect on the course of the war. The British and American armies smashed across the Rhine and were soon deep into the heart of Germany.

'Sixteen Thousand Nazi Tricks'

In Germany, the victors made one astonishing discovery after another. Gun at the ready, they cautiously made their way into ultra-modern factories deep inside old salt-mines. From crates hidden in forests and from metal drums buried in river-beds they extracted secret documents, scientific equipment, marvellous inventions and weapons whose purpose they could only guess at. In some of the deep underground workshops they came upon surviving slave laborers who had been used for these Wagnerian tasks; more dead than alive, the ragged, gaunt creatures revived at the sight of their liberators, and guided them through the labyrinth of passages to workshops containing strange-looking aircraft, fearsome rockets or peculiar submarines.

Somewhere among the millions of refugees and displaced persons streaming across Germany were the scientists and technologists responsible for these weird inventions, the men who had obeyed their masters after stifling their consciences.

The Allies could not suppress their admiration for these unfinished weapons of war and the fantastic projects which the end of hostilities had brought to a halt.

In underground factories, the first German jet-planes had been conceived: the Messerschmidt 262 to begin with, then the Heinkel 162, the Arado 234, and finally the Messerschmidt 163, in which the Nazis had placed such high hopes. Focke-Wulf had designed a jet-helicopter, and there were blue-prints of some unusual aircraft with triangular wings.

At Peenemünde, the scientists had not stopped at the V.2. An improved flying-bomb, the A.9, with a range of five hundred miles was ready to go into production. The A.10, an inter-continental missile with a range of two thousand four hundred miles, was being built; it would have carried the war to the United States. There were also a number of prototypes of more modest missiles, some ready to be mass-produced; the *Wasserfall*, for instance, a guided anti-aircraft rocket, which had several variants with poetical names – like the *Feuerlilie* (fire-lily), a product of the Hermann Goering Institute, the *Rheintochter* (daughter of the Rhine) and the *Schmetterling* (butterfly), perfected by Professor Wagner of Junkers.

At Kiel, Hellmut Walter had invented the first air-to-air missile, the HWK-509. He was also responsible for the *Panzerfaust*, an anti-tank rocket, and the catapults for flying-bombs – early versions of the catapults for jets which were later installed in American aircraft-carriers. Walter was also the inventor of the Schnorkel apparatus; this long metal tube, a kind of steel lung, enabled U-boats to remain submerged for as long as a week at a time, and greatly increased the potentiality of ocean-going submarines. Colleagues of Walter had produced several types of midget submarines, as well as a radio-controlled torpedo.

But the masterpiece of the new German weapons was a V.2 which could be fired from a submerged U-boat – a prototype, in fact, of the Polaris weapon – and which had been successfully tested in the chilly waters of Lake Töplitz, in the Austrian Alps. A new type of submarine to take V.2s within British or American waters had been ordered by Von Braun and his colleagues from the Vulkan yards at Stettin only a short time before the collapse of Germany.

Despite all these inventions of new weapons, the Germans had not neglected the improvement of conventional arms. Their technicians had even perfected the kind of gun which has long been the subject of standing jokes among the game-shooting fraternity – the 'gun which fires round corners'. Then there was a small tank filled with explosives that could make its own way towards big enemy tanks; mortars of one hundred and twenty tons and huge guns mounted on trains which could fire eight-ton shells. The Russian gunners who came across these monsters were unable to conceal their admiration. The Americans found an armored vehicle with a large, mysterious dark eye, which turned out to be an infra-red ray projector to aid artillery firing at night.

There was plenty in this German Pandora's box to amaze or instruct civilian technicians as well. An article in *Time* in 1946 was headed *Sixteen Thousand Nazis Tricks*. These tricks included a curious box-like apparatus which recorded speech and sound on a ribbon – an early tape-recorder. There were some synthetic products – mica and rubber among them – which seemed to have a future; and some electro-medical appliances, notably one which circulated ionized air among workers in factories and which the Germans called 'giver-of-heart-for-work'. German scientists had achieved the means of calming workers by feeding them this conditioned air to breathe, and of frightening them, putting them in a bad humor, or making them joyful and optimistic. The age of 'conditioned man' was on the way ...

What was to be done with all this wealth of ideas and inventions, many of which carried a strong threat of death? From the Pentagon, from Whitehall and from the Kremlin, the word went forth – *Seize them at all costs, and at once!* From Washington, London and Moscow, scientists, technologists and Intelligence officers were sent to search the ruins of the Third Reich, to be the first to gather this booty wherever it could be found. To seize these treasures was important, but it was more important still to prevent other nations from gaining possession of them. And, of course, the highest priority had to be given to laying hold of the men who had created these marvels, these dreadful weapons. In the ruins of the towns and cities, among the swarms of refugees, in Displaced Persons' camps – wherever they tried to hide or remain unnoticed – the masterminds that had almost enabled Hitler to dominate the world were to be sought out and held.

CHAPTER EIGHT

The Great Hunt

'My Name Is Wernher von Braun'

'I think you're nuts!' exclaimed Private Fred P. Schneiker.

In front of him stood a young German clad in a long black leather coat. The man had left his bicycle by the roadside and had spoken in good, though sometimes stilted English.

This encounter took place at the foot of the tree-covered slopes of the Kuhegund mountains in Bavaria. The German's words would have caused any soldier to think he was mad: 'We are a group of scientists working on rockets, and my colleagues are up there in the mountains. I want to see your commanding officer, so that we can surrender to him. One of our number is the inventor of the V.2.'

Schneiker came from Sheboygan, Wisconsin, and was not the sort to be easily impressed. In any case, this was not the first time he had seen Germans try to get favorable treatment by claiming to be people of importance. But this man insisted with such urgency that Schneiker went and told his company commander. The unit belonged to the 324th Infantry Regiment, which was the spearhead of the 44th Division. The information was passed back to Divisional HQ in the small Austrian town of Reutte, and eventually permission came for the young German to bring his friends down from the mountain that night.

A few hours later a small convoy of German army cars came down the mountain road with their headlights full on, against all military orders. The American soldiers were surprised to see a few civilians get out, all wearing the same kind of shabby black leather overcoat buttoned up to the chin. A fair-haired young man had his left arm in plaster so that he seemed to be permanently giving the Nazi salute. It was he who spoke first. 'My name is Wernher von Braun,' he told the officer in charge.

The following morning the Germans were given a large breakfast and then questioned about their identity and position. Sergeant Bill O'Hallaren, who was in charge of Public Relations for the division, found it difficult to believe Von Braun. 'He can't be a scientific genius,' he said. 'He is too fat, too young and too jovial!'

Von Braun seemed to be enjoying his first contact with the Allies. Those present could hardly believe their eyes when they saw him 'treating the soldiers with the affable condescension of some official on a tour of inspection'. He posed for photographs, smiling at the camera, and asked where this or that medal had been won; in fact he behaved more like a film star than a prisoner. He said that he would answer all questions and asserted that not only had he worked at Peenemünde but he had been the founder and the keystone of the base. This was a bit too much. 'If we haven't captured the greatest scientist of the Third Reich,' commented a GI, 'we've certainly taken its greatest liar.'

Among the group which had surrendered was a person the exact opposite of Von Braun. The Americans thought he had a 'sinister' look, and he reminded them of Eric von Stroheim. This skinny little officer was none other than the military head of Peenemünde, General Dornberger. 'We hoped that this general would storm and rage,' Bill O'Hallaren wrote later, 'but he disappointed us by his meekness and the way he sheltered behind Von Braun.'

The other scientists with these two notables were Dieter Huzel, Hans Lindenberg and Bernhard Tessmann, all from Peenemünde. Colonel Axster, one of Dornberger's staff, represented the army; and the young man with the bicycle was Magnus von Braun, brother of the great scientist with his arm in plaster.

Some American officers looking very preoccupied and secretive arrived at midday to take delivery of the prisoners.

Fred Schneiker had to wait several years before he learned that, all unknowingly, he had rendered his country the service of taking the most important prisoner of the Second World War.

The officers who had then taken charge of the prisoners were well aware of their importance. For months past, the Research and Development Service of the United States Army had been sending specially trained men to certain defined places in Germany classified as 'highest priority objectives'. The Intelligence Services had gathered a mass of information on these objectives. Among them were Peenemünde (in code – 4/95), Niedersachswerfen, Mittelwerke (4/113b), Eib Zew-Sie (4/149), and Bad Sachsa (4/96n), Dornberger's headquarters. The names of dozens of people to be arrested included Von Braun, Schilling, Rees, Riedel, Mrasek and Dornberger.

Now that the Americans held some of those at the head of the lists, notably Von Braun and Dornberger, they would have no difficulty in picking up hundreds of other Peenemünde scientists and technologists. It was an amazing stroke of luck. The group of scientists had been found not at Peenemünde, which was by then in Russian hands anyway, but in Bavaria, near the mountain redoubt in which Hitler had placed his last hopes. How did they come to be there?

The answer was readily given by the prisoners themselves. They were kept for a few days at Peiting, in a children's play center, and then removed to Garmisch Partenkirchen, where the Olympic Winter Games had been held in 1936. There they joined four hundred German scientists whom the Americans were holding in an office building of the Wehrmacht and each of the scientists was interrogated at length. In the Army Archives at Alexandria, Virginia, a big black book contains the reports of those hundreds of interrogations which revealed the secrets of eight years of feverish work within the stronghold of the Third Reich.

The Führer Had a Dream

By the time the Peenemünde base was started in 1937, the research scientists who had founded the Kummersdorf Institute in 1932 had grown from a group of eight to a company over one hundred strong. The Americans gradually learned how Peenemünde had become a vast installation with dozens of launching ramps from which bigger and better rockets were sent streaking through the sky. They learned how, on 3 October 1942, an A.4 (later known as the V.2) was sent in a flaming aureole on its first successful flight; and how a depression settled over Peenemünde after Hitler had dreamed one night that no V.2 would ever fall on London, and consequently decided to withdraw financial support from the scientists.

Every detail was brought to light in the interrogations at Garmisch: the technical and scientific problems, the conditions of work, the mechanism of the rockets, the failures as well as the successes. The reports include an account of the meeting which Dornberger and Von Braun had with Hitler, at the end of which the 'inspired strategist' was persuaded to ignore forecasts which came to him in dreams and to provide special facilities for Peenemünde. The base then developed at a great pace. Everything requested was given – tons of equipment, hundreds of research-workers and an army of slave laborers. But then Himmler decided to make Peenemünde his own preserve. He threw Von Braun, Riedel and Gröttrup into prison on a trumped-up charge of sabotage, going so far as to accuse Von Braun of plotting to fly to England in his personal aircraft with the plans of the V.2.

Dornberger had to appeal to the Führer in order to get the scientists out of the clutches of the Gestapo. He was just in time. A few months later, after the 20 July plot on Hitler's life, Himmler was successful in getting his right-hand man, SS General Kammler, appointed head of the V.2 program.

When the first rocket was fired on London, several scientists regretted that their work was being put to destructive uses. At least, they said so afterwards. But at the time it did not prevent them from celebrating the event with champagne. By then, however, it was evident that Germany had lost the war, and the scientists were fairly sure that only a few more weeks remained for Peenemünde. So they had listened somewhat sceptically to Goering's bombast when, in October 1944, wearing an Australian opossum coat and red boots, he declared: 'The V.2 is terrific! We must have it for the first Party Congress after the war!'

On the Winning Side

After the war . . . ! The leading lights at Peenemünde were already thinking seriously of that time. In January, 1945, they met secretly in a deserted farmhouse; it was probably the most secret gathering ever held at Peenemünde. The scientists present were well aware that if the Gestapo learned of their meeting and its object, they would quickly find themselves in prison, or even in the next world.

The question to be discussed concerned their future action. Germany was crumbling, the Russians were approaching from the east and the British from the west. Should they stay put and fight, should they surrender to the Russians or to the western Allies?

They could hear the ceaseless rumbling of the Red Army guns in the distance. The Russian Second Army commanded by Rokossovsky was already in the outskirts of Swinemünde, and would probably over-run the rocket installations soon. In Von Braun's office were ten orders that he had spread out on his desk. They came from different echelons of the Wehrmacht. Five of them demanded a heroic stand against the Russians; the others, less peremptory, gave opposite instructions – Von Braun and his five thousand technicians were to pack up, dismantle their equipment and move to the centre of Germany, there to continue research and the production of reprisal weapons.

A choice had to be made.

The scientists at the secret meeting unanimously voted to surrender to the Americans. The war would soon be over, and in a ruined and enemy-occupied Germany the scientists would have no chance of continuing their work. There was no question of going over to the Russians. And they had little faith in the French or the British. Besides, neither France nor Britain seemed likely to have the capital or the means, after the war, to engage in space research. So that left America.

Many years later, these German scientists claimed that, because their scientific knowledge belonged to the West, they had resolved to do everything they could to keep it on the western side of what became the iron curtain. But Von Braun, with his usual frankness, gave a different reason for his choice. 'My country has lost two world wars,' he explained. 'Next time, I should like to be on the winning side.'

On the way to Nowhere

But to get on the winning side they had to leave Peenemünde and make their way to central Germany; there they would have a much better chance of falling into the hands of the Americans. Such a journey was not easy. The German commander of the Baltic region had given the scientists strict orders to remain at Peenemünde, rifle in hand. Since 12 December 1944, the 'long-haired brains' had been receiving instruction in the use of fire-arms; they had also been taught unarmed combat and the art of street fighting. But the scientists had shown very slight en-thusiasm at the prospect of becoming an army unit.

On the other hand, the Ministry of Munitions in Berlin had decided that this unit was to be sent to Bleicherode, in the Harz Mountains. Dornberger had already transferred his HQ to that area, at Bad Sachsa. Kammler had set men to dynamiting the mountainside and making underground tunnels and caverns in which the Peenemünde laboratories were to be installed.

Von Braun and his colleagues decided to obey the order which suited them best, and prepared to move. Special rafts had to be made to take all the equipment, documents and office furniture, as well as the precious rockets, across to the mainland. The staff was sent off in lorries and trains. The documents and equipment which had to be left behind were put in drawers and crates fitted with booby-traps; when they were opened, small phials of acid would start a fire. Everything went smoothly, but one major diffi-culty remained. On leaving Peenemünde the scientists would have to pass through the area commanded by the stubborn general who wanted to see them die at their posts.

When the convoy was halted at the first army check-point, Von Braun said that Peenemünde came under the SS and insisted on being allowed through. 'We are making *Wunder Waffen* for final victory,' he told the officer.

The latter was impressed, but asked, 'What is your organization called?'

Von Braun gave the first high-sounding name that came into his head: 'Project for Special Dispositions.'

'All right,' said the officer. 'But put distinctive markings on your vehicles, and then we'll let you through.'

A few days later all the vehicles, and the crates and equipment too, bore the cryptic letters VZBV (*Vorhaben zur Besonderen Verwendung*). Notepaper, permits and travel warrants were given the heading of those four words, which were meaningless; and under their protection the convoy set off for the Harz Mountains. That was in the middle of February. Early in March, Major

Anatole Vavilov reached Peenemünde with advance elements of the Soviet Army and hoisted the Red Flag over what remained of the rocket establishment.

The convoy had to cross most of Germany, then in the last stages of defeat; because of the long straggling columns of refugees and the constant air attacks, the scientists were obliged to lay up by day and to travel by night. Von Braun dropped off to sleep in the driver's cabin of a lorry one night, and woke up the next morning in hospital, cut and bruised and with a broken arm. The exhausted driver had dropped off to sleep too.

However, they had all eventually reached Bleicherode. They unpacked their equipment and got down to work, to produce an improved version of the V.2; they also had in hand a project to supply the Wehrmacht with six hundred rockets a month – beginning in September. But before they had time to do very much, they were forced to flee again. American advance forces were reported to be in Mulhausen, less than fifteen miles south of Bleicherode!

The scientists would willingly have waited for the victors to arrive, but SS General Kammler was there to remind them that they were still in the Führer's service. He sent four hundred of the specialists by train to Oberammergau, where they were given splendid quarters in an army camp at the foot of the Bavarian Alps.

'The only disadvantage,' said Von Braun, 'was the barbed wire round the camp.'

Ominous rumors soon began to circulate: 'We're being kept here as hostages, to be handed over to the Americans in exchange for the lives of Kammler and his SS ...' – 'We're going to be exterminated, so that we shan't be captured alive by the Allies ...'

Now they had to find a ruse to save their skins. The scientists persuaded the army officers to let them disperse to the inns and hotels of the neighboring villages, so that 'a sudden air attack would not wipe out the Reich's chances of obtaining its wonder weapons'.

An ambulance was sent to remove Von Braun from the military hospital, because French troops were said to be approaching. And thus it happened that the chiefs of the biggest military scientific enterprise that Germany had ever undertaken, Von Braun and Dornberger, found themselves in the holiday surroundings of a luxurious mountain hotel, the *Ingeborg Haus*. There were some good French wines in the cellar so, with books and conversation, they passed the time pleasantly enough.

But it had to come to an end. Von Braun had decided to send his brother to meet the Americans.

The Hiding Places

The Americans were proud of their capture and kept the scientists under close guard in the camp at Garmisch. But the captors soon had a problem: what to do with idle scientists? They were asked whether they had equipment and papers. No answer was given. However, by putting two and two together the Americans learned that two or three weeks earlier some scientists and a S S detachment had hidden twenty tons of documents from Peenemünde in an abandoned mine near Nordhausen.

American forces were then in control of the Nordhausen area, but in a few days' time the British were to take over temporarily, prior to the Russians' occupying the area as part of their zone. *Would it be possible to find these documents before the Russians arrived in Nordhausen?*

When the Americans had first reached the Nordhausen area, towards the end of April, 1945, a certain Robert Staver had been on the heels of the leading units. He was head of the Jet Propulsion Section of the Army Research and Development Agency, and was a man of great initiative and independence of mind, energetic and untiring – an ideal 'scientist-hunter'.

His first 'high priority objective' was the extraordinary Mittelwerke factory, where V.2s had been constructed. He was astounded at what he saw, and immediately took up the hunt.

He ran his first scientist to earth at Bleicherode. This was Carl Otto Fleischer, a man of some importance at Peenemünde, who had not left for Bavaria with the others. Staver took Fleischer in his jeep, and together they combed the area. In an abandoned mine at Neu-Bleicherode they found the components of the *Wasserfall*, the new anti-aircraft rocket. Another salt-mine contained equipment from Peenemünde. Back at Bleicherode they had found an unexpected visitor at Fleischer's house, Eberhard Rees, the head of the testing workshops at Peenemünde. With him was one of Staver's colleagues, an engineer named Hull.

The two Germans were questioned at length, and at the end Staver was in possession of a list of twenty-five places where material and equipment had been hidden. He lost no time in visiting them all. At Leutenberg, in Thuringia, he found some valves, instruments and plans. At Lehesten there were some testing benches for V.2 engines which could be put into working order.

The bag of scientists was no small find either. It included Dr Hellmut Gröttrup and Walther Riedel, who had both been privileged to share Von Braun's imprisonment by the Nazis on a charge of sabotage. Staver found Riedel in an American-controlled prison.

A new and fascinating world opened before Staver as he questioned these two German scientists. They spoke of space travel, of inter-continental missiles, of artificial satellites and other fantastic projects, one of which was to construct an 'island in space' with a gigantic mirror which would reflect a concentration of the sun's rays onto any point on earth. By this means any country could be laid waste in a few seconds. This was to be the 'solar cannon', the absolute weapon by which Hitler had hoped to achieve mastery of the world.

As Staver had listened to these terrible and wondrous tales, and realized that these men were scientists and not crazy visionaries, he could easily see how important it was for this scientific potential to be under American control.

In the meantime, however, the urgent business of the twenty tons of hidden documents claimed his attention.

His chief, Dr Robertson, who was on a tour of inspection, brought him an important item of news: 'Von Ploetz claims that Dornberger told General Rossmann that the documents relating to the production of the V.2 had been hidden in a salt-mine at Bleicherode. Von Ploetz was the head of General Kammler's Intelligence service.'

Staver, with only this somewhat vague information to go on, decided to try a bit of bluff. While driving Fleischer and Riedel through Nordhausen he stopped the car on the main square, took a notebook from his pocket and quietly read out what seemed to be a telephone message. 'Von Braun, Steinhoff and all the scientists who withdrew to the south have been interned at Garmisch. Our Intelligence officer has been told by Von Ploetz, Dornberger, Rossmann and Kammler that a number of important plans and documents were buried somewhere near Nordhausen, and that Riedel and Fleischer could help us find them.'

The two Germans looked startled and worried. 'I'm off to have dinner now,' Staver said to them. 'We'll meet here tomorrow morning at eleven.' And he left them, wondering whether they would fall for his bluff. Luck was with him, for all unknowingly he had been speaking to the one scientist from Peenemünde who knew the hiding-place of the documents.

When Staver arrived on the square at eleven next morning he found only Riedel waiting. His eyes showed that he had spent a sleepless night, and he told Staver that Fleischer and he had been discussing extremely important matters until dawn, when Fleischer had left for the neighboring town.

Staver immediately set off after the German, but soon found that he was not running away, for at every stage he had left directions to enable Staver to follow him. Staver eventually caught up with him in the garden of a village priest. 'I brought you here as a precaution,' said Fleischer. 'It's quite true about the hidden documents. On Kammler's orders, an SS detachment loaded at least twenty tons of important files and documents on six big lorries and trailers at Peenemünde. I hope you won't hold it against me for keeping the secret until now. But as General Kammler said that I could speak, my conscience is clear in telling you. The hiding-place is in a mine in the Harz Mountains, at a village called Dornten, near Andreasberg. I'll go there with you tomorrow . . .'

The following afternoon Staver went to Fleischer's house in Bleicherode and found him sitting at a table laden with cold meats and schnaps. He was looking very solemn; he had found the hiding-place.

He had traced the final stage of the lorries, and arriving at the mine he had persuaded the manager, who was unwilling at first, to take him to the hiding place. Or rather, close to it, for the crates of documents had been stacked in a tunnel forty feet below ground. Then the entrance had been blown up, and blocked by fallen rock. 'But at this very moment,' went on Fleischer, pleased with himself for the initiative he had shown, 'three gangs of workmen are working in shifts to clear the entrance. You will have what you are looking for in two or three days.'

But it was then 21 May, and the British were due to take over the area on 1 June, soon to be followed by the Russians. *On no account were the precious documents to be allowed to fall into the hands of the Russians or the British.* Lorries were needed, but none was available. Staver lost no time; he drove to Kassel, persuaded the pilot of a P47 Thunderbolt to take him as passenger, and in the afternoon arrived, very cramped, at Orly. Half an hour later he was at SHAPE, where he obtained some trucks and two large trailers.

A few days later he reached the mine at Dornten, and found that his lightning trip to Paris had almost been in vain. While the clearing of the tunnel entrance had been proceeding under the orders of an American army lieutenant in civilian clothes, some British soldiers arrived on the scene and began searching the mine for hidden arms. The American could speak a little German. He took a chance and, with Fleischer to back him up, the two had passed themselves off as harmless geologists collecting samples of minerals. This complicity of two late enemies had succeeded in deceiving the British.

Five metal drums buried in the woods near Nordhausen were found with the aid of mine-detectors. Altogether, with the crates recovered from the tunnel, Staver had a load of fourteen tons of documents and files. He lost no time in driving away to the American zone. Behind his small convoy, British soldiers were erecting control-points and the first of the Russian troops were entering the area from the north.

The Underground Factory

It was not the first time that the Americans had played a trick on their Allies and snatched German scientific wealth right from under their noses.

On 11 April 1945, Sherman tanks of the American 3rd Armored Division were passing through Nordhausen and heading for the small town of Barby on the Elbe – where the historic junction between the advance forces of the Americans and the Russians took place soon afterwards.

The road were swarming with refugees and homeless people, and the officer commanding the leading squadron, Colonel Welborn, noticed that among them were some men in the striped garments of the concentration camps who kept gesticulating to the tank crews, as to indicate something of interest. A few of the

Americans followed them to the village of Niedersachswerfen, and found themselves at the entrance to a huge tunnel which went into the hillside. It led to a whole series of treasure caves.

'You'd have believed yourself in a magician's den,' Colonel Castillo, G-2 of the 3rd Division, said later. 'It was all as bright and shiny as in Lincoln Tunnel at New York.'

But this tunnel was much more fascinating than the one under the Hudson River. It opened into a succession of workshops and laboratories all well equipped with ultra-modern apparatus. The central chamber was vast, with a vaulted ceiling, and lit by hundreds of electric lamps; it contained an assembly line for rockets, and everything was in impeccable order, with many rockets in the production line and almost complete. It was as though the workers had just knocked off for lunch.

The discovery was reported to Divisional HQ, and top-priority messages were soon being sent to SHAPE and the Pentagon.

In Paris, a young US Army officer of Irish extraction, Major James P. Hamill, was called to the office of his chief, Colonel Holgar Toftoy, head of the American Technical Information Mission in Europe. For the past few months, Hamill and his team had been busy collecting examples of the latest German military equipment and weapons, which were then sent to the United States for examination.

This time, Toftoy had a most difficult and delicate mission for the team. He had been informed of the discovery of the Mittelwerke, the underground factory near Nordhausen where the V.2s were produced. The equipment and rockets were worth millions of dollars and represented years of research. But none of it could be touched. Nordhausen was in the Russian zone. And Eisenhower had recently issued an order that 'all factories and installations, research institutes and laboratories, patents, plans and inventions, are to be handed over intact to the representatives of the Allies'. Yet the Pentagon kept pressing Toftoy, and was now urging him to send one hundred V.2s to the United States, complete if possible.

'Jim,' said Toftoy to the young major, 'put yourself in the place of the men back home who will have to assemble these rockets again, make them work and launch them. Try not to forget any of the important parts. Oh – another thing. If you're caught at it, remember you've no right to be doing what you are doing, and that I know nothing whatever about it . . .'

So Hamill left for Germany without any official orders or backing, intending to act contrary to the express directives of the Supreme Commander. When he reached Nordhausen and went to see the underground factory, he was enraged at the idea of all that scientific wealth being handed on a plate to the Russian comrades.

He set to work at once, for the date of the Russian take-over was near. He had a Truck Company at his disposal, and he succeeded in getting another from the officer commanding at Kassel. One hundred rockets – as the Pentagon had requested – were loaded onto a special train, and two goods-trains with tankers were requisitioned to transport the liquid fuel which powered the rockets. However, Hamill had to send his trains northward, and just then absolute priority was being given to rail traffic between east and west. For four days he was stuck with his trains, unable to get them rolling in any direction. But one moonless night the area was shaken by a mysterious explosion. In the morning, breakdown gangs discovered that a small bridge of great importance in the rail-communications system had been blown, causing a hold-up in the east-west flow of traffic for a few days. An enquiry was opened, but the culprits were never discovered. The members of Hamill's team, though, knew that one of his sergeants was an expert saboteur and could always be seen with detonators and fuses sticking from the pockets of his battle-dress. At any rate, the destruction of the bridge gave a clear run for a north-bound train; and on the following day Hamill's convoy was rolling merrily towards Antwerp.

When he reached the port, the bold major sought out the two men in charge of loading operations to the United States. They happened to be American-Irish like himself. 'I need a ship to carry one hundred rockets across the Atlantic at once,' he told them. The vast amount of material already waiting for cargo-space was pointed out to him. 'Immediate and top priority,' he added. To which he received the reply: 'You're just a stupid Irishman. With one hundred rockets, your one ship would sink at once. You need at least twenty.'

In the end, sixteen ships sailed from Antwerp carrying the hundred V.2s.

However, Hamill had not heard the last of them. *In addition to disobeying Eisenhower's orders, he had short-circuited the British.* An agreement had been signed whereby half of the enemy war material captured in Europe by the Americans was to be sent to the British research services. Moreover, the latter had first claim on 'samples', and forwarded to the United States only those in which they had no interest. But Hamill and Toftoy and their chiefs had taken good care not to breathe a word of the operation to the British.

The Admiralty soon proved that it had a long arm as well as long ears. The ships transporting the V.2s were still in the North Sea when they found themselves being hailed by British warships whose captains demanded that fifty of the rockets be handed over to them! At about that time, a firmly worded British diplomatic note was being read with some irritation by the State Department in Washington. But the American military authorities refused to give way, and after much discussion the ships out of Antwerp were allowed to proceed. *The hundred V.2s were eventually landed at New Orleans.*

Three Hundred Scientists for the United States

The question of the rockets had been dealt with, but there still remained the problem of the scientists. Were they, too, to be sent to America as prizes of war? When Robert Staver had flown to Paris on 23 May 1945, to obtain trucks and trailers, he had taken the opportunity of telling his superiors of an idea he had. The German scientists were such an important capture that more should be done with them than just the questioning in Germany. Why not send them to the United States, where they could help the war effort?

Staver's enthusiasm succeeded in convincing his superiors. That same evening, a coded cable was sent to Washington, deliberately exaggerating the possibilities. 'After all, I had to sell my idea,' Staver said later. It was suggested to the generals in the Pentagon that rockets could be used against the Japanese, and that a hundred German specialists should be sent to the States at once with all their documents, plans and equipment.

Staver also told Colonel Toftoy of his idea. The colonel listened with great interest, and when Staver left Paris the following morning he left behind him a man completely won over, and determined to see that three hundred, not just one hundred, German scientists got transferred to the United States.

Things happened fast. On the afternoon of 24 May a conference took place between two groups of people several thousand miles apart. In Washington, some high-ranking officers seated round a telescripter considered the proposition being made by Toftoy and others in Paris. 'Three hundred scientists!' Toftoy repeated, when doubts were expressed from across the Atlantic. In the end, the Paris group got its idea accepted but had to compromise on the number of scientists, which was fixed at one hundred.

The following day, Toftoy sent a message to Staver in Germany: 'Paris and Washington are looking after the evacuation problem. Meanwhile, you are required to remove the German specialists and their families to an area under American control ... Let us know if you need any help ...'

The code-name inevitably given to the operation was Overcast.

Staver's idea was not altogether original. General Sommerwell had been thinking along the same lines, and on 14 May had asked the head of Intelligence at SHAPE to send a few German 'brains' to the United States. And on 18 May Colonel Donald L. Putt of the US Air Force had cabled to Washington asking permission to send five German aviation specialists across the Atlantic. Putt had added that the eminent scientist Theodor von Karmann considered that three of the specialists would save the United States at least three years of research work. While on 19 May the US Navy, in great secrecy, had got in ahead of the other services by introducing three German scientists into the United States.

The fact was that much underhand competition existed between the services, and even within each. A considerable number of technical missions and agencies were busy inside Germany: there was Toftoy's Technical Information Agency, Staver's Jet Propulsion Section, and the various teams of the Field Information Agency Technical (FIAT); there was Alsos, and the Office of Scientific Research and Development (OSRD), and the Technical Industrial Information Committee (TIIC) which was concerned with all manner of German inventions which could be used in the war against Japan.

It sometimes happened that, with so much zeal on all sides, a German was picked up who had nothing to do with any kind of scientific research except that he had the same name as some prominent scientist. Or an 'objective' was deemed important because of having belonged to this or that organization. Thus Herbert Axster was kept in the United States for two years before it was discovered that he was not a scientist at all, but a lawyer who had been on Dornberger's staff with the rank of colonel. On the other hand, real scientists were sometimes overlooked when one mission thought that they had already been captured by a rival mission.

The greatest success in the field had been the capture of Von Braun and four hundred of his colleagues by the Army; with the other specialists from Peenemünde, the US Army chiefs had a complete organization in their hands. The other services suffered from a slight inferiority complex in this matter, and began making great efforts to lay hands on a few top names in the German scientific world. The Air Force mounted Operation Lusty in mid-June, having previously been too busy with operations in the air to find time for hunting on the ground.

'The Russians Will Soon Be Here'

'You see this black line on the map?' said a staff officer to Lieutenant Morton Hunt. 'It represents the stabilization line of our advance and the Russians'. And you see this red line here? The whole area between the two lines is to be handed over to the Russians by 1 July. Now this is what we're going to do. *We're going to take all the German scientists we can find out of that area; then, with those we've already captured, they'll be sent to the States to work for us.* Some of them will be able to become United States citizens, if they wish. We've promised them that.'

Morton Hunt, who was a scientific journalist in civilian life, did not seem terribly enthusiastic for the mission, in spite of the aptness of his name.

'If you've got any moral scruples, don't let them worry you,' said the staff officer. 'You can take it from me that the Russians are doing exactly the same thing in their zone. We've got to be realistic about this!'

Hunt was given secret orders and left for Germany by road. Two days later he reported to Colonel Eric Warburg at Bad Kissingen in northern Bavaria. 'Here's a list of scientists and their addresses,' Warburg said to him. 'All you have to do is to go persuade them to come back with you here. Tell them that they will be sent to the States to work for us. Don't limit yourself to these scientists. Bring anyone who seems useful. They can come with their families and some luggage. Don't worry about political details – we'll check on all of them when we get them here.'

So Hunt set off with a lorry and his list. The first call was at Zwickau, less than a mile from the Russian stop line. But the rare birds he was after had already flown, or had been caught in the traps of cleverer poachers. Hunt turned north, towards Dessau, where he hoped to find the wife of a Dr Zindel, an engineer from Junkers who was already in Warburg's hands and had agreed to go to America.

It was six-thirty in the morning when Hunt and his driver reached Dessau, after an exhausting journey through the night. When Hunt knocked on the door at the indicated address, an elderly woman appeared – Frau Zindel herself. He told her in a few words that her husband was at Bad Kissingen and that she must join him there at once.

'But why have you called so early, and what's all the hurry?' she asked.

'The Russians will soon be here,' was all that Hunt said in reply.

'The Russians! *Lieber Gott!*' And in a few minutes Frau Zindel had gathered up all she needed and was ready to leave.

A few hours later, Hunt was outside a house in Gotha, the home of an aeronautics engineer who specialised in gliders. A dark-haired young man came to the door.

'Are you the engineer from the Gotha works?'

'Yes,' replied the young man, adding that he was a doctor of science, from Berlin, and specialized in designing wings for slow-flying aircraft.

'Would you like to come with me and work in the United States?'

The German hesitated, asked about the salary being offered and whether he would be able to take his family. In any case, he said, he would not be ready to leave for several months.

Hunt brought out his magic phrase: 'The Russians . . .'

123

An hour and a half later, Hunt was on the road again with his lorry and, in addition to Frau Zindel, he had the young engineer, his wife and two children, as passengers. To these were added a woman chemistry scientist, a professor of ballistics, and the wife of another aeronautics engineer. When they got to Bad Kissingen they were all given quarters in the *Wittelsbacher Hof*, where many other German scientists and their families were already living.

Hunt had a rest, then set off again on his collecting expedition.

A few days before the Russians arrived in Dessau – really arrived – ten US Air Force trucks were driven into the town and loaded with equipment, documents, scientists and their families. The scientists included some of the best from Junkers, those who had been working under Dr Anselm Franz, the director of the Research and Development Department.

Another eminent scientist picked up elsewhere was Dr A. Lippisch; besides being a butterfly collector, an amateur painter and a keen lute-player, he was the father of the jet-plane, the Messerschmitt 163. Then there were Hans Heinrich and Theodor Knacke, who specialized in parachutes; Dr Eugen Ryschkewitch, an expert on heat-resistant ceramic casings; and Dr Philipp von Dopp, who had constructed the Junkers' wind-tunnel.

Colonel Donald Putt himself, with other initiators of Operation Lusty, made a daring raid on the Hermann Goering Institute for Aeronautical Research in Braunschweig, despite the fact that it was in British-held territory, and went off with six valuable scientists, including Theodor Zobel, a specialist in supersonic aircraft; like his colleagues, he had been tempted by the prospect of becoming an American citizen.

However, the Red Army took over that region on 1 July, and so the hunt for German scientists had to be called off. In principle, at least; for a few bold Americans still made 'lightning raids' *in the Russian zone*, and pulled in one or two more of the scientists who had aided Hitler. These intrusions were disguised as 'courtesy visits'. But the Russians were not duped for very long, and soon established control-points on all roads to the West and had patrols guarding the frontier zone. Henceforth, the only way for German scientists in the Russian zone to 'choose freedom' was to find an escape route through the forests.

The intrepid hunters of the US Air Force were obliged to fall back on the American zone to carry out their raids. While some army officers were absent from Nordhausen one night, a group from another service tried to kidnap some of the scientists already being held. At Garmisch, where the army was keeping its finest trophies of the chase, an air-force plot to seize some of them was discovered.

The Air Force would have done better to look after its own captures. At one time there were as many as one hundred and twenty German scientists and their families quartered at the *Wittelsbacher Hof* in Bad Kissingen; despite the guard on the hotel, two French Intelligence officers managed to enter and go from room to room, talking to the scientists, casting doubts on their prospects in the United States and offering them a wonderful future in France. When the two were eventually discovered in the hotel corridors they had already persuaded a few of the scientists to go with them.

The British Borrow Some Scientists

The British and American governments had an agreement, as mentioned earlier, concerning the common use of scientific discoveries in Germany. The one hundred V.2s shipped from Antwerp to the United States had already caused a diplomatic row. The British knew about the scientists being held at Garmisch, Witzenhausen and elsewhere, and also knew that nearly all the documents relating to Hitler's wonder weapons had been recovered. The Americans wondered what attitude their allies would adopt, and were somewhat relieved to find that London showed no enthusiasm to be hospitable towards the inventors of the V.2.

However, in mid-July some British Army vehicles collected a number of German scientists from the internment camp at Garmisch and took them to Cuxhaven, in the British zone. They had not been kidnapped or handed over, but were merely being borrowed for a time. The British appeared anxious to know more about the V.2s, having previously been only at the receiving end of them, and so they had arranged a kind of congress of German scientists at Cuxhaven. A few weeks previously, the British had captured a team of scientists working there under Dr Kurt Debus. The congress lasted until September, with other German research-workers being called in. The scientists wrote long reports, taught the British all they knew about the wonder weapon, and the congress ended with a grand fireworks display – the launching of three V.2s over the North Sea. Then the British returned the scientists they had borrowed from the Americans, with their grateful thanks.

The British attitude towards the German scientists was indeed very different from that of the Americans. One evening in Kiel some British officers called at the home of Hellmut Walter, the eminent scientist responsible for a number of inventions, from a chemically propelled submarine to an anti-tank rocket. They invited him to go to London, where he would meet forty or so of his colleagues, including the aeronautics specialists Kurt Tank and Willy Messerschmitt, and the guided-missiles expert, Professor Esau.

All these German scientists were billeted in a dilapidated building in a London suburb. They were questioned at great length by a mixed commission of British, American and Canadian experts. Throughout their stay they were treated as 'enemy aliens', and at the end of it were shown round the bombed districts of London accompanied by armed soldiers. Before their 'tour', all money and papers had been removed from their pockets, in case they might try to escape.

One German scientist was given favorable treatment – Von Braun, whom the British had 'on loan' from the Americans for a fortnight. He was given quarters at a military center in Wimbledon; every morning he was taken to the War Office, where he was questioned by Sir Alwyn Douglas Crow, who was in charge of the guided-missiles program.

On one occasion when Von Braun was being taken back to Wimbledon, the RAF officer accompanying him stopped the car by some wrecked houses. The officer sat back and gave the German ample time to look at the damage one of 'his' V.2s had done in this densely populated part of London.

Off to the New World

At Witzenhausen, eighty German scientists and their families were still living in the dormitory of an old school, sleeping on mattresses on the floor. The corridors were filled with their battered suitcases and parcels, and with old, patched-up bicycles.

One day in July 1945, the men were assembled in one of the classrooms that had just been cleaned by a team of GIs. An officer had come straight from Washington to address the German scientists – Holgar Toftoy, recently promoted to be head of the Guided Missiles Division of the US Army. 'Mister Missile', as he came to be called, had won his cause and Operation Overcast had been given the 'go-ahead' by the Pentagon. In a few weeks' time, German scientists were to be sent in small groups to the New World.

An end was put to the uncertainties, the rumors and futile discussions. Each scientist in the classroom felt that a definite break had been made with the past. The Peenemünde era was over.

Another era was beginning, even more extraordinary than the last – an era in which scientists would be transplanted to the country of a late enemy, to work for him as mercenaries.

CHAPTER NINE

The Brain Mercenaries

Operation Overcast

'Ever since the four great Powers invaded Germany,' wrote a New York paper in 1946, 'Russia and the Western Allies have been waging a secret and desperate battle to capture the most eminent German scientists and their inventions. The United States has been successful in its efforts. This country has disdained reparations in money or in kind, but has rated brains at their true value.'

The American military leaders were determined not to repeat the error made after the First World War. This time, scientific research for military purposes would not be brought to a halt by the cessation of hostilities.

The decision to bring the greatest German scientists to the United States was made at the highest level. A total of three hundred and fifty was agreed upon, and these were to be allocated fairly equally between the Army, Navy and Air Force.

General Eisenhower and all the top brass were determined to make Operation Overcast a really national affair, for which not only the armed forces, but industry, the State Department and the President himself should be responsible. In this way they hoped to avoid being accused of militarism at a time when American public opinion, alerted by the revelations of the Nazi crimes, was bound to question the necessity of bringing Germans to the United States.

A decision was made to cut the pill in half, so that the public would swallow it more easily.

There would be a short-term project in which Hitler's scientists would be brought across for a period of six months; this was considered long enough to pick their brains of all knowledge useful to America's defence. Later, when passions kindled by the war had calmed down, the scientists' stay in the United States would be extended and Operation Overcast could get fully under way.

On 6 July 1945, the Combined Chiefs of Staff agreed to the terms of a secret document which provided for 'the exploitation of a minimum number of German scientists by the United States'. They would not be allowed to take their families, who would be looked after by the military authorities in Europe. The text of the document stated clearly that no war criminal was to be included, and if a scientist was later found to come within that category he must be sent back to Europe immediately.

It was this agreement that gave Toftoy authorization to set off for Europe. Before he left the United States, the fact that Operation Overcast was to remain a close secret had been strongly impressed upon him.

Major Hamill, the man who had got the one hundred V.2s to Antwerp, had asked to be sent to the Pacific front. Before leaving Europe he had gone to say goodbye to his chief, Colonel Toftoy. The latter was sorry to be losing such a valuable officer. 'Just in case you change your mind, Jim,' he said, 'here's a note for my friend Colonel van Sickel. It's about a job that's beginning to take shape in Washington.'

Hamill slipped the note in his pocket and took a plane for the United States. Midway over the Atlantic, the pilot burst into the passengers' cabin and cried: 'The President has just announced that Japan has surrendered. The war's over!' Instead of going on to Japan, Hamill went to Washington and handed Toftoy's note to Colonel van Sickel. He was given command of a rocket base which was being built at Fort Bliss.

While waiting to take up his new command, Hamill was sent to Boston to take charge of the first seven German scientists to arrive in America under Operation Overcast. He had to take them to Aberdeen, Maryland, to a secret army base where captured enemy weapons were examined and tested and new American weapons were tried out. On their arrival, the Germans were set to work under armed guard in an isolated building where all the papers and documents from Peenemünde were being sorted, catalogued and translated. It was a long and tedious task, as the papers were in great disorder, partly burned or damp – and there were forty tons of them.

One of the scientists was Von Braun, still with his arm in plaster. Hamill received orders to take him to Washington, and from there they travelled together down to Fort Bliss. Being Von Braun's guardian angel was not the easiest of missions. In the train to El Paso, a brawny Texan with his Stetson pushed back on his head turned to Von Braun with a friendly smile. 'You're not American, I guess. Where do you come from?'

'Switzerland,' answered the German, keeping his reply short to avoid revealing his guttural accent.

'Switzerland! Now that's a wonderful country,' said the Texan. And he gave a string of names of lakes, towns and mountains. 'I suppose you're over here on business,' he went on. 'What's your line?'

'Steel,' answered the reticent 'Swiss'.

'Yes, but what ... ?'

'Ball-bearings.'

'Well, what a coincidence! I make ball-bearings too. Ah, now we can compare Swiss manufacture and ...'

But the train was slowing down; the name of a station could be seen – Texarkana.

'Now that's a pity,' said the Texan. 'I get off here. I'm mighty glad to have met you. Great guys, the Swiss. Without you, those lousy Germans might have won the war ...'

Hamill had listened in fear and trembling that Von Braun would reveal his identity during the course of the conversation. After all, how far could the man be trusted? So Hamill kept close to his side, tiring though it was. 'Since I came back from Europe,' he wrote to his superiors, 'instead of being allowed to go and see my wife, I've been made to honeymoon with von Braun.'

However, the commanding officer at Fort Bliss was helpful. Hamill messed with the senior officers, while Von Braun was sent to the junior officers' quarters. The honeymoon was over. But no sooner had Hamill laid his head on his pillow than the security officer came to rouse him – Von Braun was an 'enemy alien' and so could not be left unguarded even for one night.

It was not until a few days after, when Von Braun had stomach trouble because of the unaccustomed rich food and was taken to hospital, that Hamill was finally relieved of his supervision.

The tireless Toftoy arrived at Fort Bliss just then to inspect the quarters prepared for the German scientists. He found they were only pre-fabs, totally unsuitable for these men and their work. He took Hamill with him to search the countryside for something better, and they discovered a perfect dream house, complete with patios and a swimming pool – a place for research work in ideal conditions. Unfortunately, it was an annex of the Beaumont General Hospital, and the administrators refused to part with it. Toftoy and Hamill flew to Washington and returned with a requisition order in good and proper form. The fine house was theirs, and work was at once started on converting it for use by the illustrious scientists of the Third Reich.

The Paperclip Boys

In July 1945, the scientists being held at Garmisch and Witzenhausen were given application forms for entering the United States. There was no mention of salary, and no details of conditions of work or the situation of the scientists' families. Only six completed and signed the application, which was little more than an unconditional surrender.

When Toftoy returned, a much better proposition was put to the scientists. He offered them good contracts, for a period of six months, and guaranteed that their wives and children in Germany would come under the protection of the American army. This was necessary not so much to keep watch over them as to guard them from their compatriots, who would be incensed and jealous of the favorable treatment given to families of men who had 'betrayed' their country and sold their knowledge and brains to the occupying powers.

A large number of the scientists accepted Toftoy's offer. But Washington had limited the first contingent of brains to one hundred. Toftoy managed to get this increased to one hundred and twenty-seven, but a selection was still necessary.

Cards were made out for all the applicants, listing their qualifications, their past history and so on. Each man who fulfilled the required conditions had a paperclip attached to his card, and the accepted candidates became known as 'the paperclip boys'. In fact the whole operation was given the name Paperclip.

The manner of their arrival in the United States was probably not quite what 'the paperclip boys' had expected. Some hours before the ship docked, they were all sent down to their cabins and told to remain in them. When they got ashore they had to march through back streets to coaches waiting to take them to Aberdeen or Fort Bliss. One group, which included the most eminent scientists captured during Operation Lusty, was sent to the Air Force base at Dayton, Ohio.

The top men at the Pentagon could feel satisfied with themselves. 'The British and the Russians have got hold of a few German scientists,' they said, 'but there can be no doubt that we have captured the best.'

They were perhaps presuming too much.

In Britain, during the hard winter of 1946 when coal was still in short supply, some of the public had occasion to feel indignant over the favorable treatment given to German scientists. A newspaper published a photograph of the Admiralty Hostel at Barrow, where several of them were living, showing smoke coming from all twenty-seven chimneys. So it was not enough to pay the Germans working on naval problems for Vickers-Armstrong – they had to be given abundant supplies of coal as well!

The British Government had shown little interest in the V.2 scientists, but had removed all the German naval installations of interest, as reparations, and had 'invited' Hellmut Walter and his assistants to work in England. Walter, as previously mentioned, was the inventor of the chemically propelled submarine. The first model had sunk while being tested, just before the end of the war, but frogmen had recovered it. Walter had received offers from the Americans too, but felt too old for such an upheaval and had accepted the British proposition.

The British had got hold of comparatively few German scientists at the end of the war. In addition to Walter – the one outstanding scientist – there were only a handful of specialists, notably those employed by the RAF at the Rocket Propulsion Department at Westcott, near Aylesbury. In the years just preceding the war, many German research-workers had fled from the Nazis and sought refuge in Britain; so that the Government could now declare 'it had no need of Hitler's scientists'.

The British were insisting, however, that Dornberger should be included in the war criminals to be tried at Nuremberg. But the Americans thought he could be of use to them. However, they too had to consider public opinion. Finally, they persuaded the British to place Dornberger in the P O W category, and he was sent to a camp in southern England. Two years later, some U S Air Force officers visited the camp and offered Dornberger work in America.

'I warn you,' he said. 'I cost Hitler's Germany some billions of marks. Be ready to spend billions of dollars with me . . .'

The Americans took the risk, and Dornberger went to Dayton to rejoin his colleagues.

Bridging the Rhine

Not a single German scientist had gone to France since the end of hostilities. The British and Americans had cleared out the French zone so thoroughly that such an assertion can be made without fear of contradiction. The French, however, stood in great need of German scientific brains; their own military scientific research had been reduced to nothing for the past five years. Great efforts were therefore made to lay hands on a few German scientists, even though not in the top rank, and to get them to agree to work in France, despite the hostility of the population towards all Germans.

A fortunate chance brought within reach of the French the whole team of scientists who had been working under Professor Schardin at the Ballistics Institute in Berlin-Gatow. These men had had a similar experience to that of their colleagues at Peenemünde. When the Russians drew near Berlin Professor Schardin and his assistants had evacuated their laboratories and fled westwards, eventually arriving at Blankenburg in the Harz Mountains. But the sounds of war had been heard approaching again, and from Blankenburg the scientists had gone to Unterlüss, near Lüneburg. They found themselves no better off there, and fled south to end up at Biberach, in Wurtemberg, which was included in the French zone.

When offered work in France, the German scientists showed little inclination to accept. It was then that General Cassagnou and his chief engineer officer, Fayolle, had a bright idea. As the Germans feared the hostile attitude of the French population and preferred to continue living in Germany, it might be possible for them to work in laboratories in France from homes just across the frontier. A detailed study of the map revealed three possibilities of such an arrangement: Strasbourg, with a bridge across the Rhine to the German town of Kehl; Neuf-Brisach and the opposite town of Alt-Brisach; and the area of Kembs. But Strasbourg was over-populated and Neuf-Brisach was in ruins. Near Kembs, however, in the town of Saint Louis, was a large, empty factory which could be converted for the purpose, and there was a technical school which might provide some skilled workmen; and a bridge across the Rhine led to two pretty villages, Weil and Haltingen. Three universities were within reach – Strasbourg in France, Basel in Switzerland, and Freiburg in Germany – and their scientific libraries would facilitate research.

This arrangement reassured the German scientists, and they signed what must be the most curious contract given to any of the 'brain mercenaries'. Under the terms of this contract, the scientists would live with their families on the German side of the Rhine, where housing would be found for them. Coaches were to fetch them in the mornings and bring them to Saint Louis to work, and to take them back home in the evenings. This was done so discreetly that the local population never became aware of what was happening. And the German commuters enabled the French to set up an Armaments Research Laboratory.

However, this was far from sufficient. 'The French were in such great need of scientists,' said a British specialist in the subject, 'that they were offering work to qualified Germans without restrictions of any kind. But the Germans did not conceal their apprehensions. Some hesitated two or three years before agreeing to go to France.'

An article on Diesel engines published in a German magazine put French Intelligence on the track of its author. He was found to have been one of the scientists at Peenemünde, a Dr Fritz Pauly. Two French Air Force officers went to see him and offered him a contract with a company making jet-engines, which he accepted. He was soon joined by others, including a few who had been rejected by the Americans when the list of 'paperclip boys' was being established, and who were beginning to be anxious about their future as scientists. Then there were some whose connections with the Nazi Party had landed them in an Allied internment camp; by the time they were released, the British and the Americans had enough German scientists, so this group readily accepted the offers from the French. This was the case with Hellmut von Zborowski, an aviation specialist, who had been interned for having joined the Waffen SS in the final stages of the war.

Zborowski was born in Bohemia of a long line of scientific engineers; there was even a legend that one of his distant ancestors had invented the horseshoe at the end of the tenth century. His great-great-grandfather, certainly, had been a mining engineer, and his great-grandfather had been ennobled by Emperor Francis-Joseph for building the first Austrian railway. His father had been in command of the first airship built in Austria; and he himself had shown his worth by his work on the jet Me 163, the *Schmetterling* rocket and other weapons. By 1945 he had one hundred patents to his name.

Two years after the end of the war Zborowski started work in France, and designed one of the most amazing aircraft ever, the Coleopter, a vertical take-off plane with a cylindrical wing enclosing the fuselage like a barrel. Two of his wartime collaborators went to France with him – Dr Wilhelm Siebold, a specialist in aerodynamics, and Professor Heinrich Hertel, who had been director of research at Junkers.

Two research-workers who had been together since 1942, Eugen Sänger and Irene Bredt, were married in Paris in 1946 and spent their honeymoon at the French Air Force Aeronautical Arsenal at Châtillon. Sänger, a friend of Zborowski, specialized in supersonic wind-tunnels and was full of ideas, the least fantastic being a 'flying-wing' propelled by powerful rockets which would be able to circle the world. Irene Bredt had worked with him on this project. Sänger soon became a picturesque figure in French scientific circles, with his thick mane of hair and bushy eyebrows, and his visionary ideas on the conquest of space.

Many other German scientists joined these early few. Specialists on infra-red rays went to work in French Navy laboratories near Paris; the aircraft industry employed Germans in the development of rocket motors. Rolf Engel, one of the founders of the almost prehistoric *Verein für Raumschiffahrt* and a member of the Research Council of the Third Reich, was given an advisory post with the National Aeronautical Research and Study Office in Paris.

German engineers less well-known were set to work at Vernon,

Normandy, on a project which became the *Véronique* rocket. Then there was Wolfgang Pilz, a minor light from Peenemünde; blue-eyed and wavy-haired, with a handsome profile, he looked like a romantic hero, a Werther of the atomic age. Pilz was already thinking of space rockets and satellites. His close collaborator, Goerke, was more realistic and concentrated on guided missiles. While Hans Kleinwachter, whose eyes always seemed cloudy behind his spectacles, specialized in acoustics and radio-communications. He had spent the early part of the war in Dresden, working for the army on some research for which he felt little enthusiasm – transforming household refuse into pig food. He had later served on the Russian front as a major in the Signal Corps. And now, after the war, the French were employing him on guided missiles, although his real interest was in the use of acoustics to invent a guide-system for the blind.

Elsewhere in the World

Many names have been cited, but a number of Hitler's scientists were still missing from the scene. Where was Kurt Tank hiding? What had happened to Rudel, Galland and Baumbach, all aces of the Luftwaffe? And to Willy Messerschmitt? He and Tank, it will be remembered, had both been taken to London for a time. Then the famous aircraft constructor had succeeded in getting to Spain, or so it was said. While Tank, who had been the chief engineer at Focke-Wulf, had completely disappeared after his release from an internment camp.

The great majority of German scientists had accepted their country's defeat philosophically – amazingly so, in many cases. They had effected a small inner revolution and gone over to the service of a late enemy. But there were some, more true to themselves or perhaps nostalgic for Nazi times, who had sought a distant refuge where it would not be shameful to have been a Nazi, or even to remain one. For there was such a country – Peron's Argentina, which was quite ready to give a friendly welcome to scientific geniuses of the Third Reich. In fact, Peron's agents went to Germany to contact Nazi scientists, technicians and engineers who had not gone to work for any of the Allied powers. Those who accepted Peron's offers were supplied with false passports and smuggled into Denmark, and from there were flown to South

America. Another underground route was through the Austrian Tyrol and northern Italy to a Mediterranean port.

These Germans arrived in Buenos Aires expecting to find good working conditions and a pleasant atmosphere, to be allowed to wear their Nazi decorations openly, even if they could not flaunt the swastika. But nearly all of them were deeply disillusioned. The Argentinian aircraft industry was insignificant compared with that of the great powers, and was unable to absorb several hundred engineers and pilots in such a short time. Only the really great specialists and the outstanding test-pilots found employment. Dr Armin Dadieu, an ex-Gauleiter who had escaped from Germany under the name of Rudolf Schober, was one of them. And Kurt Tank, who turned up there, was made head of the technical section of the Research Institute, and was eventually responsible for Argentina's first jet-plane, the *Pulqui*, a fighter aircraft with a speed of seven hundred m.p.h.

Other German scientists went to South Africa or Brazil, or went into hiding in Switzerland. A few ended up in Australia or New Zealand.

The Allied Military Control in Germany had prohibited scientific research for military purposes by any German scientist in the homeland. Unable to follow their careers, most of the scientists left the country without any real prospects, some with nothing more than the clothes they were wearing, trusting in their lucky star.

One of these was Hermann Oberth, who had been much less guilty than most of the scientists caught up in the Nazi web. Oberth, a Rumanian by birth, had been forced to take German nationality; the alternative, he did not doubt, was a concentration camp. He filled a secondary role at Peenemünde until 1943, when he was given a chance of realizing his dream of making a solid-fuel rocket. He left Peenemünde for Wittenberg, on the river Elbe, and threw himself wholeheartedly into the task. But his laboratory and the factories supplying him with materials were destroyed in air-raids. He was interned at the end of the war and questioned at length; after his release he fell on hard times, and managed to cross the frontier illegally in hopes of earning a living in Switzerland as a consultant engineer. By then, he was getting on in years, poor and lonely. Eventually he found work with the Italian Admiralty, which realised his value and sent him to the research establishment at La Spezia. There, assisted by three German engineers and five Italians, he was at last able to develop his solid-fuel rocket. Then he returned to finish his days in Germany.

Enter the Russians

However, the British and American secret services and military research establishments were not anxious about people like Oberth, Tank, or even Messerschmitt, but about the scientists taken by the Russians; just who they all were was not known, and even less certain was their particular line of research. But, from information gathered during the final stages of the war, the British and the Americans had little doubt that the Russians were concentrating on atomic research.

At the end of April, 1945, during the battle for Berlin, special Red Army units had surrounded the Kaiser Wilhelm Institute – where, six years previously, Otto Hahn had first split the atom. Russian officers had gone straight to the basement and taken away the cyclotron; with great care, it had been sent to the rear, and eventually to somewhere near Stalingrad.

Another unit had descended upon the Research Institute at Lichterfelde where Baron Manfred von Ardenne was working. He was arrested, together with thirty-five of his assistants, and all of them vanished from Germany. The Russians had made an important capture, from which they soon profited.

Von Ardenne was a remarkable scientist. He had built himself a radio-set when only twelve years of age, and had then invented a number of ingenious instruments and gadgets for which he had taken out patents. He was too intelligent for the normal school curriculum; he had taught himself all he knew. He had his own laboratory, in which he built a large cyclotron, an apparatus for the acceleration of protons, an electronic microscope ... He began to be called 'Atom star'; it was he who, just before the war, had given the idea of making an atom-bomb to Minister Ohnesorge. And now that the war had ended it appeared highly probable that he would make the bomb – but not in Germany.

Another eminent atomic scientist in Russian hands was Gustav Hertz, a Nobel prize winner. He had refused to join the Nazi Party, and so had been removed from his university chair. Other scientists in Russia included Professors Bewilogua, Peter Thiessen and Fritz Vollmer, and dozens of their assistants.

There were certainly many more. Agents from the Russian zone were known to have been going around Western Germany offering research-workers high salaries to go and work in Russia. Despite the security measures of the British at Göttingen, where the German physicists had been allowed to go after their internment in England, Soviet agents managed to approach Werner Heisenberg. 'They promised me six thousand dollars a year,' he revealed, 'fifty pounds of fresh meat a month, a ration scale of 13,500 calories for each of my six children, and a comfortable house to live in . . .'

Heisenberg declined the offer, but several of his colleagues were tempted and, depressed by the hard conditions of life in post-war Germany, finally accepted similar propositions.

The Allies knew that the Russians wanted to make an atom-bomb at all costs, and that they had a great need of 'brains'. Information reaching Allied Intelligence indicated that the USSR had annexed the 'Independent Republic' of Touva, which had once been a province of Chinese Mongolia, because of the rich uranium deposits in the mountain ranges. The uranium mines at Joachimstal and in Saxony were being worked to full capacity by the Russians. More significant still was the feverish activity reported from Czechoslovakia, near the town of Podmokly, where the river Elbe runs down from the Sudeten mountains. Six miles from Podmokly was the Weser underground factory, deep in the mountain-side. The Russians had discovered several V.2 fuse-lages and a mass of documents in this cavern; but the most interesting discovery was that huge cyclotrons were made there.

The Weser factory was silent for several months after the end of the war in Europe, but soon after the A-bomb was dropped on Hiroshima the factory was started up again with the same German engineers in charge, but working for a new master. Cyclotrons were again being constructed, to be sent this time to the shores of the Black Sea. It was there, in the delightful surroundings of an ex-royal palace at Agudzeri, near the resort of Soukhoumi, that the Russians were installing their nuclear laboratories. Scientists brought from Germany started work in the great marble halls of the buildings set among palm trees and exotic gardens. Tales reached the West that Von Ardenne and Hertz were making components for A-bombs, but informed observers believed they were engaged in perfecting cyclotrons and other research apparatus.

There was also a vague report on the mysterious Zimmermann – the man believed to have invented the 'death ray' and even to have used it effectively against the Russians in the Carpathians on 30 August 1944. The report said that he had been captured and taken to Russia just before the end of the war. And was it not true that the Peenemünde scientists rejected by the Americans had gone to work for the Russians, with Hellmut Gröttrup at their head? There were certainly loud-speakers making enticing offers from the Russian bank of the Elbe to any 'brain' on the other side who cared to cross over.

However, the Americans did not pay much attention to these reports. In the first place, it was known that most of the scientists working for the Russians had remained in East Germany; their laboratories and the factories supplying them with materials had simply been rebuilt. And then, as *Time* proclaimed with obvious satisfaction late in 1946, 'We have got hold of the best brains.' Proof of this was that in May 1946, V.2s transported to the United States were already being successfully launched from bases in New Mexico.

Washington in Trouble

Soon after the first German scientists had arrived at Fort Bliss, the authorities prepared for the second stage of Operation Paperclip, which included the naturalization of the new immigrants.

Secretary of State Byrnes feared that if the Germans returned to Europe at the end of their six months in the States, they would fall into the hands of the Russians. It was therefore necessary to bind them to the United States in a permanent manner. But strong opposition to the proposal came from some high Government officials and diplomats who, during the war, had belonged to the 'Safe Haven' movement, the aim of which had been to prevent the Nazi ideology from spreading to America. And now it was proposed to give full rights in the American community to people imbued with Nazi ideas!

There was dissension at the Pentagon too. Some of the generals did not hide their opinions on the subject: 'These scientists are mercenaries and nothing more! Are there no physicists in America, that we really need these Germans?"

One answer to that question was given a little later by a test-flight of the Hermes missile, which had been developed and built entirely by American brains. The launching was a great disappointment. Hermes hardly got off the ground, and crashed on the base itself.

A committee representing the Army, Navy and State Department eventually produced a 'basic policy'. The title of the document, which remained on the secret list until quite recently, was 'Exploitation of German and Austrian scientists within the framework of the Paperclip project'. The 'exploitation' was to be carried out by the Departments for War, the Navy, and Trade, in coordination with the British. There would be a list of scientists – never to exceed one thousand names – to be communicated to the Combined Chiefs of Staff, the security services and the FBI. The Germans selected would be allowed to have their families join them at the end of a probationary period.

The Commander in Chief of the US European Theater of Operations would give contracts specifying salary and conditions of work, with clauses covering the return to Europe of scientists whose stay in the United States was not extended. The scientists and their families were to be under military control until they obtained their visas.

There was a special clause dealing with the thorny problem of ex-Nazis: 'No person may be allowed into the United States who has been a member of the Nazi Party and has taken more than a nominal part in its activities. . . . However, an appointment or distinctions given by the Nazi regime entirely for technical or scientific ability will not in themselves disqualify the specialists having received them.'

On 13 September 1946, Dean Acheson placed the document before President Truman for his signature, and on 24 October the 'Declaration of Basic Policy' came into force. That same day, the news that German scientists were working in the United States was officially released.

A great outcry followed. The weekly magazine *The Nation* published an article headed 'This Brain for hire – Memo to a would-be war criminal'. Its author, J. Joesten, made some caustic remarks – to be a war-mongering politician was no longer safe, for

> if you lose, they'll hang you. If you are a general and lose, they'll shoot you . . . But if you are a scientist, you will be honored, regardless of who wins. Your enemies will coddle you, and compete for you, no matter how many of their countrymen you may have killed.[1]

Other articles similar in tone appeared in the press, and newspapers received a flood of letters. Congressman John Dingell indignantly exclaimed: 'I should never have thought we were so intellectually poor that it would be necessary to import men to defend the United States.' Leagues and committees for the defense of democracy started a crusade. The president of the American Jewish Congress, Rabbi Wise, sent a confidential letter of protest to the Secretary of State for War, Robert Patterson. But the greatest indignation came from the humiliated American scientists.

Their reaction was natural enough. They were opposed to the subjection of science to the military authorities and to research for military purposes in times of peace, and had still not recovered from the shock of the many thousands killed by the dropping of the atomic bombs over Hiroshima and Nagasaki, for which they felt morally responsible. Some scientists emphasized that much of the research in Germany was carried out by men who had undergone the formative influence of the Hitler Youth movement. Others recalled that Von Braun and many of his colleagues had joined the Nazi Party in 1940 or even earlier. And how many of the Peenemünde scientists had declared themselves devoted, body and soul, to their Führer?

'The German scientists imported by us are not superior to our own radio-technicians,' said one American scientist. 'At best, they are only skillful engineers,' declared another. 'At least, don't call them scientists!' implored a third.

The Federation of American Scientists issued a manifesto in which it denounced 'the importation of second-hand scientists, which is contrary to the noblest objectives of American policy,' and declared it to be 'an affront to all nations which recently fought at our side.'

[1] *The Nation*, January 11, 1947, p. 36.

An avalanche of letters reached the office of the Secretary of State for War, from private individuals and from organizations. But the decision had been made and could not be reversed. Officials pointed out that although some Nazis might have slipped into the herd, each applicant was subjected to a most penetrating examination. 'The Gestapo examined the files on them too, and found no blemish,' retorted the American scientists.

It was the Russians who, paradoxically, provided the American Government with the strong argument needed to quiet this storm of protest. The Cold War started in 1947. Dreams of eternal peace were shattered, and the opposition was reduced to silence by statements that the German scientists were contributing to the defense of the Free world.

The Germans are Americanized

The children of the Germans at Fort Bliss and at Dayton often returned from school crying, complaining that they were called 'dirty Nazis' and set upon by their classmates. Their parents could only tell them to be patient.

Security measures had been very strict at first. The Germans were not allowed to leave camp on their own, and those at Fort Bliss could go to the nearest town of El Paso, on the Mexican frontier, only under guard. Letters and parcels were censored. The FBI had to be informed whenever the scientists' work required them to make a journey, and a watch was kept on them at all times.

However, after a while, passes were given to them with ever greater frequency. The Germans at Fort Bliss were allowed to have their own club in a wing of the Beaumont hospital; and when their families arrived, several floors of the annex were made into apartments.

The constant use of the American language by day, and lessons and films in the evenings, gradually reduced the use of German between the scientists themselves. They picked up some army slang from the soldiers. Thus, when Von Braun had to go to the Pentagon to make a report, his superiors dreaded that he might come out with a few barracks expressions in front of the worthy generals. In any case, he had acquired a Texan accent. The Germans – familiarly addressed as 'Carlo' or 'Rudy' by the soldiers – soon took to wide-brimmed hats and cowboy boots, and became appreciative of the tortillas and Mexican *enchiladas* served in El Paso restaurants. Secondhand cars began to be seen in front of the annex.

These exterior signs of assimilation were, however, somewhat deceptive. The scientists still retained their Teutonic sense of discipline and rigid respect for the hierarchy. Among them, a man with a mere science degree would never dare take precedence over a Herr Doktor, and the latter would respectfully give way to a Herr Professor; while everyone almost genuflected before Von Braun.

When their situation became established, a few of the scientists were given permission to visit Germany for urgent reasons. The American authorities there kept a very close control over them; they were forbidden to go near the East German frontier, and Berlin was definitely 'off limits'. The authorities could take no risk of their being kidnapped by the Russians. Von Braun had become engaged to a cousin, by letter, and was allowed to go to Bavaria to marry her. As the couple came out of the church they found an American guard of honor drawn up, ready for any eventuality.

The Peenemünde scientists transplanted to the United States were undoubtedly doing good work; great progress was being made in rocket propulsion, and larger, more powerful rockets were being developed. At the same time, the German scientists and their wives were producing children; and these births were being duly registered at the local municipal offices. This raised a problem for the officials – how could these American births be shown when the parents were not legally in America at all? The scientists had in fact been brought into the country as 'special employees' of the Army, without passports or visas. They and their wives therefore had no legal existence, but it was not until 1948 that a decision was made to put an end to this absurd situation.

A day came when the whole German colony at Fort Bliss got into a bus and went across the bridge from El Paso to the Mexican frontier town of Ciudad Juarez, where they all trooped into the US Consulate. They filled in application forms, were at once given visas, and then returned as legal immigrants to the country of their adoption. The operation had taken only a few hours, and there were some odd details on the immigration forms – Port of departure: Ciudad Juarez. Port of arrival: El Paso. Means of transport: town bus service, El Paso. Cost of journey: four cents.

Everything was going well by this time. The public had long forgotten or ceased to care about the problem of the Nazi scientists. At the Pentagon, at Fort Bliss, Aberdeen and Dayton, the military expressed every satisfaction with the work of the 'Rudys'. The scientist-hunters could rest content too; they had done an excellent job. No one in authority paid any attention to a secret report from a source in West Germany which was based on a conversation with a young German engineer named Werner Singelmann. He worked in East Germany and, so he said, had been roused from his bed at four in the morning and put on a train, together with hundreds of other technicians and engineers, headed for the Soviet Union. But Singelmann had managed to jump off the train. He had been the only one to do so; the others, thousands of specialists, he said, were taken to Russia.

In Washington the report was read with a smile. Great progress was being made at Fort Bliss and elsewhere. 'We have the best of the scientists,' repeated the military leaders. 'We're well ahead of the Russians!'

F

CHAPTER TEN

Five Thousand German
Scientists for Stalin

The Russians Have a Rocket

'Faster, faster, and faster still!' In the middle of an arid plain stood a lone tower, and near it there were tall, cone-tipped cylindrical objects pointing skywards, all guarded by barbed-wire and sentries. The first light of dawn was spreading over a vast tented camp. Soviet Army trucks were dashing along between the rows of tents marked 'Made in USA', and snowploughs were being used to flatten down the sandy soil. The plain was crowded with men, thousands of them.

An icy wind was blowing across the Kazakstan steppes. Red Army soldiers, muffled up in thick coats and fur caps, mingled with the local *moujiks*. There were Pioneer squads from Stalingrad, scientists from the Moscow Academy, and engineers with Teutonic accents. In a few hours the cold arctic night would give way to scorching heat. By midday a swimsuit would seem too much to wear. And a huge meal would have to be eaten, enormous portions of rice and mutton.

The men near the tower and the big fuel-chambers appeared to be on edge, and kept cursing in Russian or German. An official plane landed on a makeshift runway, bringing a group of generals and civilians. One of them was the Minister for Munitions, Mr Ustinov, to whom were presented Herr Doktor Gröttrup, Herr Doktor Wolff, Dr Albring, Dr Umpfenbach and several others.

What exactly was happening on this day, 30 October 1947, in a remote part of Central Asia?

Only that the first Russian rocket was about to be launched.

The tower had been constructed with sections brought from Peenemünde and was not very stable, but it stood. The previous evening, a workman on the scaffolding had fallen sixty feet and broken his neck. An iron bar had dropped from the tower and killed the officer commanding a detachment of Pioneers. Then the control equipment had developed a fault, and German electronic experts were hurriedly fetched from Moscow in the middle of the night. The stability of the gyroscopes seemed doubtful, and the Russian officers were tending to look askance at the Germans, with the word 'sabotage' on their lips. Others were whispering that the Minister for Munitions had promised a bonus of one hundred thousand roubles if the experiment was successful.

The rocket could be plainly seen on its launching-pad, and wisps of white smoke were beginning to issue from the tail of the huge cyclindrical propellant. Then...

Suddenly the rocket tottered as one of the supports of the tower began to give way. Heedless of the danger, soldiers dashed to the scaffolding, climbed up and made the necessary repairs. The count-down began again, heard by the spectators through loud-speakers. 'Now!' The order rang out. And the rocket roared up to the sky on a splendid jet of flame.

A cheer rose from eight thousand throats. Ustinov hugged the director of the base, who then turned to hug Hellmut Gröttrup, the chief engineer, and exclaimed: 'You see! Russian rockets are better than German ones!' But someone in the group of scientists could not help remarking: 'The Russians have nothing to do with it. German scientists did it all, with purely German equipment.'

However, Russia could take credit for this successful launching. *It crowned a vast effort which had started as the war was ending.*

A Present from Eisenhower

At the end of 1944 the Kremlin had set up a 'Special Department' and put Georgi Malenkov in charge of it. His directives were clear – to seize all industrial and scientific equipment which might be of military use to the USSR, under the title of reparations.

The Russians had decided on a wholesale operation. Not only were the factories, workshops and research laboratories to be dismantled, and thousands of tons of machinery, tools, raw materials and documents to be taken to Russia, but the Russians also wanted the men capable of coordinating it all.

As soon as Berlin had fallen, a special unit moved in to carry out this specific task. Its commander, Colonel Shostock, had little information to help him in his mission, much less than his American opposite number had; there was no unit so well briefed as *Alsos* on the Russian side. The capture of Von Ardenne, Hertz and Thiessen was merely a stroke of luck. Moreover, there was a lack of liaison between the 'Special Department' and Army HQ, as evidenced by the fact that the first officer to reach Peenemünde, Anatole Vavilov, had orders to destroy the base and all its equipment. Thus, lacking definite instructions and sound information, and moving among people who hated them, the Russian agents had no easy task.

It was therefore with surprise and delight that Shostock's second-in-command, Lieutenant-Colonel Wladimir Shabinsky, discovered the extensive Mittelwerke plant at Niedersachswerfen, its huge workshops, assembly halls and rockets in course of production. How could the Americans have been so stupid as to leave all that untouched when they evacuated the region three days before? 'They'll be sorry for it, in ten years' time,' remarked the colonel. 'By then our rockets will be crossing the Atlantic!'

When Major Yegorov (a member of the special section of the NKVD) brought back lorry-loads of documents from the Mittelwerke and hiding-places in the Harz Mountains, Shostock celebrated the event with a banquet at Marshal Joukov's HQ. While proposing the toast, Lieutenant-Colonel Tarakanov repeated the theme 'How stupid these Americans are!'

The Americans had shown that they were not so stupid as all that. But they had not fully grasped the fact, as the Russians had done, that *in the next war rockets would be the major weapon.*

The discovery of the Mittelwerke was a great incentive to Shostock's men. They went at once to Peenemünde, and managed to save two research laboratories and to collect a few launching ramps, dozens of V.1s and V.2s and anti-aircraft missiles. At Lübeck and Magdeburg they found the huge barges loaded with rockets and fuel that Von Braun had succeeded in sending across to the mainland. They combed the Harz Mountains, which yielded an abundant store of documents and equipment. In a research station near Nordhausen they found plans of Hellmut Walter's *schnorkel* device for submarines and of other inventions of his. The Russians 'visited' the Zeiss laboratories and Professor Esau's Physics Institute at Jena, the Siebel aircraft factory at Halle, the Heinkel factories at Warnemünde and Oranienburg, and the Junkers factories at Bernburg and Dessau; also the Raabe Institute for rocket propulsion at Bleicherode, which was found to be intact; and the Messerschmitt factory at Wiener Neustadt, the Arado aviation works at Babelsberg, the Dornier factory at Wismar, the Henschel works at Erfurt and in Berlin ... Two-thirds of the German aircraft industry had fallen into Soviet hands. But the most important of all was still the Mittelwerke plant and the well-equipped factories and workshops in the Harz Mountains, which Eisenhower, like a perfect gentleman, had left for his Russian allies.

Twenty years after the end of the war, several Allied statesmen and military leaders were still criticizing Eisenhower for having made this present to the Russians. And the corridors of the Pentagon long echoed with General Vandenberg's protests. He repeated to all and sundry: *'The Germans were ten years ahead of us, and we have graciously made a present of them to the Russians!'*

However, at the time, the Russians were still searching for the men who could teach them how to make use of all these riches. They were up against the great difficulty that practically no 'long-haired brains' were left in the Russian zone. Nearly all had fled to the West before the approaching Red Army. Few indeed were the scientists who believed that Marxism would rule the world and so stayed behind. Fewer still were those who went over to the Russians because they remembered past hopes that the Weimar Republic and Revolutionary Russia would form a good alliance.

The Russians could not indulge in the luxury of a chase *à la* Pash, nor could they hope to be so overwhelmed by a rush of scientists that they would have to choose among them by attaching paperclips to their cards. For the time being the Russians had to be content with small fry.

The Phoenix Rises from the Ashes

'Herr Hans Kuhl?' asked the smiling young Russian officer at the door. Behind him in the street was an American jeep marked with the Red Star – one of the presents to Stalin under Roosevelt's Lend-Lease agreement.

How had the Russians found out that Hans Kuhl was living in the small town of Jüterborg, south of Berlin? Simply by getting his address from the Telefunken in Berlin. They had then lost no time – the date was 15 June 1945.

'Herr Kuhl, would you care to resume your work in the V.2 control mechanism section? We are in the process of starting up the plant again. You could begin work at once . . .'

This Russian lieutenant was not at all like the 'big bad wolf' of Goebbels's propaganda. He was polite and attentive, answered questions and promised wonders. Kuhl would have a good house, a high salary, food and tobacco, and be working with the same team as before.

'Yes, that's fine,' said Kuhl. 'But what about these rumors of deportation to Russia?'

'Oh, there's no question of that,' answered the lieutenant.

Hans Kuhl could not resist the temptation, and a few days later he and his family moved into pleasant quarters at Hohen-Schönhausen, just outside Berlin. He found himself working with German engineers and technicians and Russian scientists who spoke fluent German. Kuhl was delighted with this turn of fortune, and agreed to accompany some high officials to Peenemünde to help them unearth some apparatus and measuring instruments which had been hidden. On his return, he set to work and explained exactly how they all worked. The Russian scientists stuck close to him and other German technicians – of which there were many! Some arrived every night in closed lorries, settled into charming houses and began work at once. There was little else they could have done. They realized they were trapped, although the Russians had behaved so politely. But how had these Russians found out where all the German technicians, great and small, were living?

They had practically gone from door to door in every town. They had spread their net everywhere, questioned prisoners, officers and officials, scoured POW and DP camps. And who at that time would not have accepted an offer of work which meant comfort and liberty?

'Liberty' was perhaps an exaggeration. The living quarters, comfortable though they were, had barbed-wire round them and were guarded day and night by armed sentries. However, it was better than a camp or starvation. Thus protected, the research centers of the Third Reich were revived, rebuilt – the Raabe Institute at Bleicherode, the GEMA laboratories near Berlin, and those of the great aircraft and electronics industries, even Krupps.

Meanwhile, agents were discreetly knocking at doors in the Western zones, promising 'El Dorado' to scientists they found; and they succeeded in bringing over to the East a first small instalment of 'brains'. Powerful loud-speakers were set up on the east bank of the Elbe, and for days blared out: 'Where is Ernst Steinhoff? Does anyone know Steinhoff's address? A big reward will be paid to anyone giving news of Steinhoff!' Thus did the great expert on electronics learn that a price had been put on his head. He managed to avoid being caught, but the Russians did get a consolation prize – Steinhoff's chief assistant, young Hellmut Gröttrup, who was an excellent scientist but a difficult character to deal with. Strangely enough, it was to a great extent thanks to the Americans that the Russians were able to get hold of him.

As already noted, Operation Paperclip covered a limited number of scientists. Only three hundred and fifty, out of the thousands of technicians and research-workers that the German defeat had reduced to idleness, eventually entered the United States. Of the five thousand Peenemünde scientists, only one hundred and twenty-seven crossed the Atlantic. All the remainder, when released from the Garmisch and Witzenhausen internment camps, disappeared into the blue. They were free to go where they wished, even to cross into the Russian zone.

The first to go over to the Russians was Hellmut Gröttrup. The Americans had thought him quite worthy to have a paper-clip on his card, but Gröttrup refused to be separated from his wife and two young children even for a short period. He would have preferred to work in England or in Germany.

Somehow or other the Russians learned of his attitude and were soon at his door. General Gaidukov offered to put him in charge of the Mittelwerke plant, which by then had been re-named Zentralwerke. 'We guarantee that you will not be de-ported,' Gröttrup was told. 'You can go on working in your own country.' Gröttrup was young and ambitious, but fully realized that he was selling his soul. Whoever helped him would necessarily become his master.

Nevertheless he went to work for the Russians. The vast sums of money allotted to him enabled him to attract many of his old colleagues to the factory in the Harz Mountains, once it had been started up again. The Phoenix had risen from the ashes! Specialists arrived to join Gröttrup from all over Germany – from universities and research institutes in central and even western Germany. Only a few months after taking up his post, *Gröttrup had under him more than five thousand technicians and scientists,* the most notable of whom was Dr Waldemar Schierhorn, the wizard of aluminium alloys. There was also Dr Albring, who had been head of the Institute of Aerodynamics at Danzig and then production chief for the Linke Hoffmann heavy industries; Jochen Umpfenbach, rocket propulsion expert, Mueller, Magnus, Hoch and many more . . .

Results from this concentration of 'brains' were not long in coming. A complete V.2 was built at the Zentralwerke, soon fol-lowed by ten, twenty, hundreds of rockets. These 'first fruits' were sent to the USSR, where Russian scientists examined them, then tried a few launchings to get their hand in. *The Russians caught up the eight years they had been behind the Germans in a matter of months.*

The Russian supervisors at the Zentralwerke were less in-terested in constructional process than in production methods, organization and the use of equipment and instruments. They rained questions on their German colleagues and insisted upon long written reports. It was not long before they were quite at home in the underground labyrinth.

The men in the Kremlin decided that the time had come for the big sweep.

In the Bag

On the evening of 21 October 1946, General Gaidukov, the Russian overlord of the Zentralwerke, gave a banquet to two hundred German scientists and engineers. They had spent the day in study groups, and the conversation at table turned on past successes and future plans. The dinner was copious; there were Bavarian sausages and Caspian caviar, Rhine wines and vodka. The Germans gradually became bemused, and not one noticed that Gaidukov's aide-de-camp kept bringing him messages.

At dawn, Irmgard Gröttrup was wakened by the telephone. She reached for the receiver, and could only make out the end of the message: 'You are being taken to Moscow too.'

She was still wondering what it was all about when she heard a loud banging on the street door. She went to open it, and there stood Russian officers with the usual courteous smiles.

The following day, railway workers at Brest-Litovsk saw *ninety-two special trains* pass through the station, speeding eastward. They were all packed with men, women and children. In fact, they were carrying between fifteen and twenty thousand people, the entire personnel of the armaments industry and their families.

The Russians had just rounded up five thousand 'brains'. But it was no brutal, inhuman deportation. The planning had been done several months before. Then, during the night, troops had silently surrounded the houses and been posted at the doors. The operation had started at exactly 04.15 hours.

A few Germans had tried to protest or argue, but it was no use. The soldiers had their orders and were there to carry them out. The scientists' equipment and apparatus were already being removed, and the installations at the vast Niedersachswerfen plant were being completely dismantled, as was all the apparatus at the Raabe Institute in Bleicherode. The Zentralwerke had ceased to exist as such.

The officers who had organized and successfully carried out this huge and complicated operation were heartily congratulated. Everything had gone off well; there had been no need to resort to force or physical violence. A few mistakes had occurred, inevitably; some people who had nothing whatever to do with science had been taken away, two or three families had become separated, and one or two daring young engineers had managed to jump from the train and escape through the forests into West Germany. But on the whole, the collection and removal of these twenty thousand people had gone off according to plan.

As far back as the spring of 1945 Moscow had decided that the post-war military program would be directed towards the development of rockets and supersonic aircraft, which would be built on Russian soil but with materials seized in Germany. The men in the Kremlin had quite realised that to transfer all the scientific treasures as soon as hostilities had ended would be quite useless. Blast furnaces and chemical plants could be removed and then be operated by Russians, but it was a different matter with the intricate machines and precision instruments used in the production of rockets and aero-engines. Scientists could not be expected to turn themselves into skilled workmen. So the Russians had first to learn how to use this delicate machinery, and the best way was to watch the Germans. Once the factories started up again, and the Russians had mastered the production methods – then would be the time to dismantle and remove everything to Russia with the greatest precautions.

The men in the Kremlin thereby proved themselves to be more wily than their counterparts in the Pentagon. Von Braun and his colleagues were for a long time dissatisfied with the facilities and credits allocated to them, and also with the conditions of work they found in America. It was only after several years that they really started to be 'productive'.

The Russians requisitioned whole residential districts on the outskirts of large towns, and chose the sites for the new factories with great care.

The German scientists and technicians had no idea of their destination as they looked from the train windows at the Russian plains slipping past. During the journey, Gröttrup held a meeting of his heads of staff for the purpose of drawing up a protest to the Russian officials. Red Army soldiers were distributing tea, soup and bread, clambering over luggage and stepping past sleeping children. A Dr Ronger, whose wife had died three days before the round-up, said that he had been wakened at his home by a Russian officer who had orders to collect two people. 'Take any woman,' the officer had told him. 'You can marry her at the other end.' Another engineer, whose wife had been away at the time, had been taken with his housekeeper, a pretty young woman who told everybody on the train that she would soon be 'Frau Doktor'.

The corridors were buzzing with rumors – that they were being taken to the Urals ... to Central Asia ... perhaps to the

Volga.... Some pessimists said they were being taken to an extermination camp. No, they were going to be received at the Kremlin, replied the optimists, who were very few in number.

The trains finally drew in at Monino station, not far from Moscow. There was a reception committee waiting on the platform, stamping their feet against the cold; they were officers from the 'Special Department'. They saw that everyone got out of the trains and into army lorries, and conducted the exiles to their new homes.

Most of the Germans found themselves in cramped living conditions, but the Russians respected the hierarchy; Gröttrup and his family were given a large, six-room house which had once been the home of a Minister. Answers were readily given to the Germans' questions: personal belongings would arrive in a few days; salaries would, in general, be four times those paid to Russian engineers; work would begin at once. For the Russians tried to make their enforced guests forget as far as possible that they were just prisoners. They knew from experience that a liberal attitude, absolving the Germans from any material worries, was bound to pay dividends.

The Gilded Cage

The atomic scientists who had been taken to Russia more than a year before were indeed spending happy days on the shores of the Black Sea. As far back as 1934, the Soviet Union had started this 'gilded cage' system. The first to experience it, ironically enough, had been a Russian physicist named Piotr Kapitza who had emigrated to Britain after the Revolution. When he unwisely went to Moscow on a visit, the authorities took away his passport, saying that he was needed in his native land; the Russians were already anxious about the Nazi menace. The contents of Kapitza's laboratory were sent to Russia from England, the British authorities having courteously agreed to this on receipt of thirty thousand pounds sterling. The physicist was provided with modern scientific equipment, given a house and two cars – quite something in the USSR in 1934! He soon became one of the leading nuclear physicists, and did not appear to miss the London fogs very much.

The German scientists in their turn took possession of magnificent laboratories, where the entrance-halls had marble columns and red carpets but also stocky militiawomen armed with revolvers. 'It will be another Peenemünde,' said the Russians. Not long afterwards, some of the Germans were astounded to hear a hawker crying his wares: 'Here you are – steel false teeth! Guaranteed made with steel from genuine German V.2s!'

Some of the exiles had difficulty in swallowing the pill, well sugared as it was. 'Why am I here?' Gröttrup said to Ustinov one day.

'Aren't you in charge of rocket development? The reconstruction of the V.2s is almost complete. You've just got to give orders.'

'When shall we be going back to Germany?'

'When you can fly round the world on one of your rockets, Herr Doktor,' Ustinov slyly replied.

A few days later he summoned Gröttrup and the senior staff to his office. 'I am handing back your protest, gentlemen,' he told them, 'as there are no grounds for it. Under the Potsdam agreement, Russia is allowed to bring five thousand people from Germany and to use them on reconstruction.'

'But we're not engaged on reconstruction,' Gröttrup coldly replied. 'We are doing highly specialized work.'

'Perhaps you would rather be sent to the Urals, and do piecework?'

'And the women and children who were deported with us?' pursued Gröttrup. 'Are they mentioned in the Potsdam agreement?'

Ustinov, a plump little man with a pleasant expression, was not to be drawn. 'The USSR respects men's rights and has not broken up the families. Do you realize, Herr Doktor, that you are the only one to complain like this?'

Gröttrup did not easily give in; his stubbornness was well known to his colleagues. Von Braun said of him: 'He's the sort who lashes out whenever anything doesn't suit him. He believes in personal freedom.'

But Ustinov firmly put an end to Gröttrup's protests by saying: 'I would remind you that the Soviet Union won the war. And I must impress upon you that no protests are allowed in Russia. One word from me, and you and your men will find yourselves transferred to the Ministry of Mines. In any case, you have signed this letter of protest in your capacity as head of the

Zentralwerke. I would remind you that the Zentralwerke, as such, has officially ceased to exist.'

Gröttrup retained his position as head of the organisation and spokesman for his colleagues, who also kept the positions they had held in Germany. But the Russians began to apply the principle 'divide and rule'. They spread rumors that it was Gröttrup who fixed his subordinates' salaries, decided on their living conditions and privileges. They also put it about that Frau Gröttrup was very extravagant and that her husband lived in the greatest luxury. These stories met with most belief at the ballistics research station which had been set up some two hundred miles north of Moscow, on the little wooded island of Gorodomlia in the middle of Lake Seliger. In winter, wolves sometimes crossed the frozen lake in search of food in the island village.

Still, the Germans were working. Some of their apparatus had got lost in the move, so they made replacements which were an improvement on the old. As one of the scientists remarked: 'I sometimes wonder whether the Russians held back our apparatus purposely, so that we could make something more up-to-date ...'

A year passed, and on that 30 October 1947, the first rocket 'Made in USSR' soared up to the Kazakstan sky. The Germans were jubilant – it was their work, their achievement; now they would be allowed to return to Germany.

But they did not know that the farsighted 'Little Father of the people' was not at all inclined to part with them.

CHAPTER ELEVEN

From v.2s to Sputniks

To the Moon

At the end of November 1947, Stalin presided over a meeting at the Kremlin which included Molotov, Malenkov and Beria, Marshals Voznessenski and Voroshilov, and the dictator's son, Vassili Stalin.

Two Air Force officers, Colonel Serov and Lieutenant-Colonel Tokayeff, were called in to read their reports on the launching of the V.2 the previous month. All those present were highly satisfied, with the exception of Malenkov. 'This rocket has no strategic value, its range is too limited,' he said. 'What good is the V.2? We won't be fighting Poland in the next war, will we?'

The two officers stuffed their reports back in their brief-cases. But the meeting was not yet over; in fact, the chief reason for it had just been reached. The members listened for half an hour while Tokayeff gave details of the Third Reich's most secret wonder-weapon, a rocket-plane.

This was the project that Sänger and his assistant, Irene Bredt, had been working on in 1944. One hundred copies of his secret report had been printed, all stamped *Geheimsache U.M. 3538*. They were circulated by hand, and among the names on the restricted distribution list were those of Heisenberg and Von Braun. Some copies fell into the hands of the British and Americans at the end of the war; they put their 'Top Secret' stamps on them too, and filed them away in their research centers. One copy, however, was discovered by the Russians among the papers of a German scientist they had captured. In less than a month it reached Stalin, who gave orders for a translation to be made.

And now Tokayeff was commenting on it and explaining the possibilities.

Stalin was most impressed. 'With this plane carrying an atomic bomb we could become masters of the world,' he said. He ordered the two Air Force officers, Serov and Tokayeff, to leave for Germany with his son, Vassili, and to find Sänger at all costs; then they were to bring him to Russia, by force if necessary.

Two days later the three were in Berlin. They found no trace of Sänger there, and Tokayeff crossed into West Germany with papers showing him to be harmlessly engaged as a member of the Repatriation Commission. He travelled all over the Trizone for three months, searching for news of Sänger but without success. Despite all their efforts, the Russians never discovered that Sänger was working in Paris. His project was revived ten years later, when the space-plane 'Dyna Soar' was being planned; but until then it remained dormant. As for Tokayeff, he apparently thought he would do well not to return to Russia and confess the failure of his mission; he went over to the British in 1948 and told his whole story.

The Russians decided instead to build up an air force of modern jet-bombers and supersonic fighters comparable to those of the Western powers, and to intensify the rocket program. For the latter, the German scientists would again be required in a major role.

A meeting of the Scientific Council was held on 12 December 1947, at the new laboratories in Moscow. Seated round the red baize-covered table were senior army officers and officials, scientists and directors of ZAGI, the Central Institute of Aerodynamics. Gröttrup was present too, with his chief assistants, and he spread out the design of a new rocket, the R.10, which would have three times the range of a V.2.

A couple of days later the Russians and Germans were again seated together, at another banquet. Glasses were raised and toasts proposed with great enthusiasm. 'To the moon!' was the oft-repeated cry.

The German rocket specialists were sent to Gorodomlia, which had become a 'little Germany'. The houses had neat little gardens, and the women wore colorful Bavarian skirts and hats from Berlin. The men worked on the new rocket by day, and met at each other's homes in the evenings to listen to music or play chess.

Their salaries had been reduced and food stores on the island in the lake were low, but the Germans went on working in the hope that when their task was finished they would be allowed, this time, to return to Germany. They found some comfort in the letters that reached them from their ex-colleagues now in the United States. In that affluent democracy the German scientists were under military control too, it appeared, and were not paid very much; nor was it certain that Von Braun was any better thought of in the United States than Gröttrup was in Russia.

The winter was very severe at Gorodomlia. Now and again the Germans crossed the frozen lake to visit the nearest town of Ostashkov, always under escort. They mingled with the crowd, but children followed them through the streets shouting 'Nazis! Nazis!'

However, Russians came to join the island colony in increasing numbers. They were all young men, keen and intelligent, and studied the German scientists' methods of work down to the smallest details. There could be no doubt that in a year or two these young engineers would be fully capable of taking over in the space race from their late enemies. Proof of this was given early in 1949, when the R.10 was developed. The Russians then carried the original project no farther, but adapted some of the ideas to a rocket of their own design. Gradually, the rockets which had seen the light of day at Peenemünde were acquiring Russian nationality.

But the former enemies were still needed. In April 1949, Ustinov arrived at Gorodomlia by helicopter. 'We want a rocket with a range of two thousand miles,' he told the Germans, 'a rocket that can carry a war-head with three tons of explosives.'

The Germans wondered whether this project had any connection with the rumor that the Russians were about to explode an atomic bomb developed by Von Ardenne. But Ustinov was not about to enlighten them.

The torrid summer drew to an end, winter approached again, and the Germans were still on the island in the lake. They were drinking heavily and beginning to neglect their appearance. Russian scientists continually visited them, asking all manner of questions, while from Moscow came written demands for precise details, reports and designs.

To their great surprise, the Germans were told that they were not required to be present at the test-flight of the new rocket, he R.14, which they had designed. It was being assembled at Tallin, in Esthonia, and at Uralskoie in central Russia. At the launching-sites on the great wide steppes, the Russians were becoming increasingly proficient.

Gröttrup was getting nervous and irritable once again. The Russians had asked him to improve some detail of the rocket. 'How can I do that?' he said testily, 'when I know nothing about the experimental launchings? What do the Russians take us for? Electronic brains, walking encyclopedias?'

The Return to the West

The R.14, was completed during the summer of 1950. Before the end of the year, a Soviet commission decided to send a score of the Germans – the least important among them – back to Germany. Russian specialists soon took charge of all the installations on the island of Gorodomlia, and the Germans of the 'other Peenemünde' began to receive some strange requests. They were asked to supply such things as a statoscope for aircraft, an adding-machine, and an amphibious vehicle propelled by rockets and which could travel over ice. The German scientists quickly got the impression that they were considered little more than museum-pieces, and were being kept for fear they would set to work elsewhere.

The Russians indeed had no desire to release these men who could tell the West some of the secrets of the strategic plans of the USSR. So they were kept 'on ice' for another two years. In November, 1953, another Soviet commission arrived in Gorodomlia and all the Germans were summoned to hear the decisions. The children hid under the benches at the back of the room. With beating heart, the exiles listened while a list of names was read out, and then heard the following welcome words: 'All the German scientists previously mentioned [only a dozen names were missing from the list] will be returned to their own country, beginning on 22 November 1953. They must be out of the

Soviet Union within forty-eight hours of that date. We take this opportunity of thanking them for the work they have done.'

That was all.

The following day, Gröttrup and his battalion of 'brains' started their return journey to the West.

German specialists were being repatriated from many parts of Russia, now that they had divulged all their secrets. They had been taken from their homeland after making the V.2 and were being returned to it after producing the R.14, which had a range ten times as great and could kill three times as many people. The specialists who were being sent home from Soukhoumi and Sotchi, the atomic scientists, were as sun-tanned as people returning from a long holiday. Their chief, Gustav Hertz, one of those captured by the Russians just before the end of the war, had long been thought dead. The first news of him had come from a Swedish scientist who had received a letter posted by Hertz in Moscow; the envelope had contained the photograph of a thin man, gaunt but apparently in good health. Now Hertz was returning to Germany covered with honors and medals and the recipient of a Stalin prize.

A few months later came the turn of Von Ardenne, 'der rote Baron', as his friends began to call him. The Russians, as well as the Americans, had had their aristocratic scientist. In East Germany he was allowed to keep his title, and newspapers sometimes referred to him as 'comrade baron'. A fine house was built for him, with stables for his horses; the Communists were so grateful to him that they forgot their principles in his case, and he was permitted to indulge in the aristocratic pastime of riding.

The Russians began to repatriate another large group of Germans once the rocket-scientists had been returned. This second contingent was made up of men from the aircraft industry, the technicians, draughtsmen, engineers and test-pilots who had built up the Luftwaffe and produced the wonder-planes which Hitler had thought would sweep the enemy from the skies.

These men, the cream of Junkers, Heinkel, Siebel and other aircraft factories, had been taken to two villages one hundred miles north of Moscow, built on the shores of an artificial lake called Podberezia. By October, 1946, there were more than two thousand Germans and their families living in the rows of small brick and timber houses which Russian workmen had built in a matter of weeks. When the Germans started work they had a great surprise; each man's desk or work-table was complete with his papers and instruments as he had left them at Dessau, Oranienburg or Leipzig. It was as though everything had been transported by the sweep of a magic wand.

The chief engineer from Junkers, Dr Brunolf Baade, became head of 'No. 1 Construction Department'. The Russians had seized the prototype of the JU.287, the first German jet-bomber, and it was standing in a hangar. Its test-pilot, Kapitan Dülgen, was able to continue with it as though work had merely been interrupted by the holidays. He took off from Nikolovaskoye, the experimental airfield outside Moscow, and the plane's performance filled the Russians with joy and high hopes. Baade was told to continue on the same lines, with the object of providing the Soviet air force with the long-range bombers so badly needed.

Meanwhile, powerful aero-engines were being brought down the Volga on rafts, to be tested in the wind-tunnels at 'Little Germany' – as the Podberezia villages had come to be called even in official documents. The engines were being built at Kuybyshev, where eight hundred German engineers and technicians worked under the orders of a ruddy-faced giant of a man, Ferdinand Brandner. He was an Austrian who had been responsible for Junkers' 3,000-horsepower jet-engine, the Jumo 222. The Russians discovered him in a POW camp in the Urals – Brandner had been a colonel in the SS – and in 1948 he was brought to Kuybyshev, where a senior official from the Air Ministry made a bargain with him. 'Your freedom and that of your colleagues for the most powerful turbo-engines you can make. We'll give you five years to do it.'

'What did helping the Russians matter to me?' Brandner said later. 'The important thing was to get away from the Urals and to return home to Germany one day, with my men.'

In September 1950, Brandner had a 6,000-horsepower engine ready for the Russians. Four years later, this had been developed into a 12,000-horsepower turbo-prop-engine. The fuselages made by Baade and the turbo-engines by Brandner were combined, after many modifications, to produce the Tupolev 114, one of the biggest transport planes in the world, and the twin of the

163

Tupolev 20 bomber – which was called the 'Bear' by NATO Intelligence officers.

Neither Baade nor Brandner was present at the first flights of their enormous aircraft. Baade had been given a post at the Institue of Aerodynamics in Moscow, and Brandner was back in Germany. During the summer of 1954 he and his eight hundred colleagues had passed through the Iron Curtain. To be exact, not all the eight hundred returned with him; twenty-five had died in Russia, five had committed suicide and two had gone mad.

'Sabre' Against 'Mig'

The Russians had another jet-bomber, the 'Bison', with a long slim fuselage and swept-back wings. But the 'Bear' and the 'Bison' needed a supersonic fighter to protect them. However, no magician capable of pulling this out of a hat could be found among the German specialists at Podberezia. So the Russians had gone hunting again.

A few weeks after the majority of the Germans had settled in at Podberezia, an army car arrived late one night with two passengers. By dawn, the news was all over the colony – Dr Benz and Professor Siegfried Gunther had come to join them. The following day, the two started work.

Gunther must have been especially surprised at finding himself by the Volga. As soon as the guns had ceased firing in Germany he had made his way to the nearest US Army HQ and politely asked to be directed to the scientist-recruiters. He was sent to Landsberg, where he produced all his qualifications – professor of science, chief designer for Heinkel, where he had been responsible for the first jet-plane, the He.178, and the He.162, among others. The He.162, or *Volksjäger*, also called the supersonic Volkswagen, had been Goering's last card; it was designed, tested and built in the incredible time of ninety days.

Gunther had been quite sure that the Americans would welcome him with open arms, but he was disappointed. His professional record seemed too good to be true, and he was politely shown the door. Disgusted with this treatment, he went to East Berlin, where his father-in-law ran a garage. Less than forty-eight hours after his arrival he was roused in the middle of the night – a Russian officer was asking to see him. 'Major Valentin

Sokolow, engineer,' the officer introduced himself when Gunther appeared. A few hours later, Gunther and his wife were in one of the offices of the Russian High Command. Gunther found himself in the company of Dr Benz, who had collaborated with him on the *Volksjäger*; Benz, too, had been hauled out of bed. A senior Russian officer promised them all manner of advantages if they would go and work in the Soviet Union.

Before they could give an answer, they were taken to Schönefeld aerodrome and flown to Moscow. Less than twenty-four hours after being roused from their sleep, they found themselves at Podberezia.

Four years later the Korean War broke out, and US fighter-planes were soon coming up against swift opponents in the shape of the Russian 'Mig 15'. The Western powers already knew something of this fighter; their military attachés in Moscow had seen it flashing across the sky at over seven hundred m.p.h. during army parades in Red Square, and agents had obtained a few blurred photographs of its sleek, bold outline.

The Americans sent their latest supersonic fighter, the 'Sabre F.86', to Korea to meet the new threat; and they were greatly relieved to find that the 'Sabre' was superior to the 'Mig'. But the American fighter-pilots soon became aware of an odd resemblance between the two types – in fact the only apparent difference was that one bore a blue star and the other a red star. To tell friend from foe, at the speed and height at which the fighters flew, was often extremely difficult; so the Americans had secret orders to give a recognition signal by dipping their wings when a jet-fighter was sighted in the Korean sky. If no answering signal was given the other could be taken for an enemy 'Mig' and appropriate action could be taken.

But how had this close resemblance between the two types come about? A German historian, Werner Keller, investigated the subject, and in his book[1] he quoted from an article by Frank Campion which appeared in *Life* in February, 1952.

During the summer of 1945, according to this report two interesting items were sent to the North American Aviation Coy in Los Angeles by Air Force Intelligence. One was a wing from the latest German jet-fighter, the Messerschmitt 262. It was made

[1] *Ost minus West - null* (Munich, 1963).

in the shape of a bat's wing, and nothing like it had been seen before. The other thing was a secret report describing the results of German tests with a swept-back wing. These two elements saved the North American at least three years of research in developing the Sabre F.86. The Russians had found the same information in the files of the Luftwaffe.

It would therefore seem that the 'Mig' and the 'Sabre' were both of German descent, and *symbolized the dispersion of German scientists to either side of the Iron Curtain.*

But can it be said that the Tupolev 114 was the work of Baade and not of Tupolev? That the Mig 15 was designed and built by Gunther and not by Mikoyan and Gurevitch? Neither Baade nor Gunther saw the final results of their work. Each was present at early test-flights, and had perfected the various parts, the wings, fuselage, engines, etc. But then each had been removed from the over-all direction before the stage of building a prototype was reached. These scientists and their German teams had been replaced by the Russian engineers who for many months had stood behind them; and the final stages were completed far from 'Little Germany' and the Nikolovaskoye airfield.

When the Mig 15 appeared in 1949, not one of the Germans could recognize it as the aircraft on which he had worked. Nevertheless, aircraft engineers in West Germany, Ernst Heinkel among them, were quite definite in their opinion. 'The Mig is Gunther's plane,' they said. But when Gunther got back to Germany in 1954 he was equally assertive, though perhaps a little dogmatic. 'I did not build the Mig,' he maintained.

The mystery has never been solved.

By the spring of 1955 all the Germans taken to Russia appeared to have been returned to their homeland. The adults had acquired some knowledge of the Russian language, and the children knew more about the history of the Communist Party, from their attendance at Russian schools, than they did about Frederick the Great. The eldest among them had studied at Leningrad University. However, the authorities had taken care to maintain a barrier between the Germans and the Russian people. When the repatriated Germans were asked by journalists whether any of their colleagues still remained in Russian hands, they could only reply with a shrug of helplessness.

Unknown to them, a small team of Germans was still being

held by the Russians – a 'brains trust' of radar and ballistic specialists.

Under the Palm Trees of Soukhoumi

A few German scientists had been kept behind at Gorodomlia in case any unexpected problems arose. After a few months, the head of the little colony, Hans Hoch, was summoned to Moscow and was told he would not be returning to the island; his position there was being given to Dr Waldemar Wolff, who had been head of the ballistics department at Krupps.

The next surprise for Hoch came when he was taken to his new quarters; they were in a pleasant district of the capital, and he found several radar specialists and experts on pilotless planes already living there – two Germans, Faulstich and Eitzenberger, and an Austrian like himself, Dr Buschbeck. A number of other eminent German scientists, who had previously been at Gorodomlia, Monino or Kuybyshev, were there too. The team was under the personal authority of Minister Ustinov, and an affable, cheerful Russian was in charge of it; the Germans had already nicknamed him 'Bubi'. He was in fact the son of the most feared man in the Soviet Union, Lavrenti Beria, the chief of police. Was his presence intended as a warning to the ex-enemy scientists?

The problems with which they had to deal were of capital importance to the Russians; but the Germans only realized this when the first Sputnik went into orbit, on 4 October 1957. Until then, they were kept in ignorance of the ultimate use of their research, and the orders they received could be summed up in two words – 'Work fast!'

They did so, in an old, disused factory at Lossino-Petrovsk. Stalin died, and Beria did not long survive him, but the German scientists worked on.

A commission visited Lossino-Petrovsk on 30 June 1955, to put some of the scientists 'on ice', so to speak, although actually they were packed off to the shores of the Black Sea, where the temperature was then well over ninety degrees Fahrenheit. The Germans were upset by the heat and humidity and unable to do any work, other than flip through the pages of scientific journals. But nothing more was asked of them. 'Have a rest, go for a swim, take a stroll,' they were told. 'Continue the pleasant life you had in Moscow, here under the palm trees of Soukhoumi.' Their salary reached them regularly; the tailors along the Russian Riviera were expensive but their suits were well cut, and Armenians had some splendid carpets to sell.

All the German scientists working in or near Moscow gradually arrived at Soukhoumi, the last of them on 12 September. The following day, on reading the papers, they understood why they had been packed off to the Black Sea. That morning, Chancellor Adenauer was arriving in the Soviet Union on an official visit. The men in the Kremlin would be able to say to him, quite truthfully: 'There is not a single German scientist left, for hundreds of miles around.'

Adenauer returned to West Germany, but the German scientists continued their idle days at Soukhoumi. They were visited by a commission now and again, which left them sometimes filled with hope and sometimes completely despondent. 'It's of no importance if these men waste a few years of their lives,' the Russians told each other. 'What matters is that they should forget all they have learned of our secrets.'

However, in August, 1956, a small group of them was sent to East Germany but strictly forbidden to cross the demarcation line to the West. Those remaining had the consolation of being told by the Russians: 'You will be going back home when the devil turns pure white!'

In January 1957, a Government decision was communicated to the remaining Germans: 'You will be able to return to East Germany, provided you do not cross to the West before the end of 1958.' In September, 1957, came another announcement: 'You will all be back home before the end of the year.' In January 1958, the waiting period was reduced to three months – and only five weeks later all the German scientists had been returned to Berlin by train.

In the meantime, a great event had occurred in the history of mankind. The Russians had put Sputnik One into orbit.

This was undoubtedly the reason for the liberation of the last of the German scientists at the particular time. President Eisenhower pointedly said: 'Ever since 1945, when the Russians rounded up all the Peenemünde scientists, the Soviet Union has been concentrating all its efforts on rocket missiles.' It seemed that the President was not fully aware of what was happening in his own country; and certain Americans commented: 'Ike doesn't know what he's talking about – the Peenemünde scientists, Von Braun and company, are in our hands!'

The American public was greatly disturbed by the news of Sputnik One. But Bob Hope made the most apt comment, in one of his TV shows. 'It's quite simple,' he said. '*Their* Germans are better than *our* Germans!'

CHAPTER TWELVE

The Scientific Spies

The 'American' Rocket

When the news of the first Sputnik reached Von Braun in Huntsville he turned to his chief, General Medaris, and said, 'Give me eighty days, and we'll have a satellite in orbit too.'

Eighty days had already been given ten times over – but not to Von Braun and his team.

In the struggle which had been going on among the heads of the three services at the Pentagon, the Navy had emerged victorious. But the Vanguard, which was intended to be the first earth satellite, never got higher than the trees in Californian orchards. Even so, the Americans had not been too worried about their setbacks, so sure were they of their superiority over the Russians. And it was only the launching of Sputnik Two that roused them to give Von Braun the free hand he wanted.

Modifications were quickly made to a Redstone rocket, which was a direct descendant of the V.2. William Pickering and James Van Allen filled it with measuring apparatus, and on 31 January 1958, Explorer One went into orbit.

A French humorist said that if the two earth satellites happened to meet in space they could greet each other with a friendly 'Guten Tag'. The Sputnik's German might have a Russian accent, but then the Explorer's would have a Texas drawl.

The Russians, however, stated emphatically that the Sputnik was entirely a product of Russian technology and no foreign scientist had had a part in its construction. This was probably true; as already noted, they had drawn the necessary knowledge from the German 'brains', and then gone ahead on their own.

The Americans had gone about it in a very different way. Their imported scientists lived quite openly in America, and it was no secret that they had built the Explorer. But it could be fairly claimed, too, that the Explorer was American to its aerial-tips, because Von Braun and his colleagues had become United States citizens.

This assimilation of immigrants was, after all, part of American policy and tradition. The Russians had kept their German scientists behind barriers, but those in the United States had been able to live the life of the people. In order to help the process of integration, the authorities had sent them to Huntsville. This town had been named after John Hunt, a veteran of the War of Independence, at which time it was the temporary capital of Alabama. During the Second World War the Army decided to make Huntsville the center of production of the means for chemical and bacteriologic warfare – should this ever become necessary, despite prohibition by the Geneva Convention. The arsenal got its name of Redstone from the color of the rocky earth on which it was built. Prosperity thus came to Huntsville, but after the war its population began to wonder about the future. In the democratic way of good Americans, they approached their Senator on the subject; he promised them that the arsenal would be taken over by the Air Force. This was good news, as undoubtedly Air Force personnel would spend more money in the town than munition workers. However, like many other promises made by politicians, this one was not kept; instead of American airmen, German scientists and their families came to live in the town.

'Germans? The last time our boys saw any, it was to shoot them,' was the reaction of the people of Huntsville. And when Von Braun and his colleagues set foot in the town they soon realized that they were not exactly welcome.

It was the first time they had been left to their own resources, so to speak, since their arrival in America and their four years in the isolation of Fort Bliss. They had proved their loyalty to the Stars and Stripes, so there was no need to keep them in a military camp any longer. Since they wanted to become real Americans, the sooner they took the plunge into the American way of life the better for them, particularly as their new homes would be more spacious and modern.

The authorities had not foreseen the reaction of the people in Huntsville. They pretended not to understand the newcomers' English, gaped at their pompous politeness, and giggled at the German women noting down prices on their shopping-list to get the best buys. The first impulse of the Germans was to keep to themselves, but Von Braun and some of his friends thought that once the first shock was over it would be far better to mix with the community.

They were quite right, as events were to prove. After a few years, Huntsville was a changed town. Many German names figured among the members of its institutions and charitable organizations. There were always whipped-cream cakes made by German women to be had at church fetes. The municipal orchestra was much larger, and the town's splendid ring-road was the work of Hannes Leuhrsen, the architect who had planned Peenemünde. Pumpernickel and sauerkraut had made their appearance on American tables, and there were many shining Volkswagens in the carparks. The lovely Monte Saro, on which Von Braun and Dr Stuhlinger had built their houses, was called 'Sauerkraut Hill' by the locals. And when American nationality was granted to the scientists, on 14 April 1955, the Mayor of Huntsville gave a touching speech which brought tears to the eyes of several old ladies.

The American people's generous feelings had brought about a near miracle. But it was a very different matter where work was concerned. The ex-German scientists were constantly complaining about insufficient credits, the difficulties put in their way by the bureaucrats, and the indifference to the rocket program in government circles. 'If we had been listened to,' one of them said later, 'the United States would have had an inter-continental missile in 1950.' But in 1945 Dr Vannevar Bush, the chairman of the OSRD, had said: 'I'm fed up with hearing about a rocket missile with an atomic war-head and a range of three thousand miles, which will hit a named target in another continent. Nobody in the world today can achieve such a thing. And I bet we won't see anything like it for a very long time. It'd be a good thing if the American public stopped hoping for such an achievement.'

Yet, less than ten years later, the Germans (*ours* and *theirs*) were to prove him mistaken. And the scientists, on both sides of the Iron Curtain, did not hide their satisfaction. These rockets ushered in the era of space exploration, but they were also terrifying weapons of war. The Germans had had their Black Sea villas and Armenian carpets, their houses on 'Sauerkraut Hill' and their United States passports, and in return they had done the work asked of them. They had actually been encouraged to pave the way for the push-button war; *they had been a sort of Foreign Legion of modern science, supplying the Russian and American giants with the weapons for an atomic apocalypse.* But they were beyond realizing this.

Scientists and their Consciences

'Scientists are the mercenaries of modern warfare,' began an anonymous article in *The Christian Century* in June, 1948. 'Almost wholly devoid of humanitarian impulses, they consider their cold and analytical search for scientific knowledge more important than any current affairs of mere mortals. If a scientist is given a chance to pursue his line of research unmolested, he doesn't care about the type of government he is working under, or the condition of the people, or anything else. Science is the thing, not people . . .

'Give a scientist a problem, any problem, and he is happy. During the war it was the problem of killing people in greater numbers than ever before. The scientists went at it with a vengeance. They came up with schemes that military men never dreamed of . . .

'Certainly they are responsible for the uses made of their discoveries; certainly they can control how their new scientific principles are utilized; certainly they have to consider the implications of their research and not merely strive blindly for facts, facts, facts.

' . . . There is a positive step which scientists who want to prove that they are not mercenaries might take. They might take a stand against the continuation of military research. They might urge their fellow technicians to stop making more bombs. They might indeed stop supporting war, either directly or indirectly, while sending out lofty declarations about peace. The people want our scientists to do more than damn the use of yesterday's weapons. They want them to stop making new weapons for new wars.'[1]

The writer of this article was an atomic scientist, one of those whose consciences had been stricken and who had suffered torments of soul-searching.

The bomb which the scientist had given to the world seemed to boomerang on them. American journals compared them with Prometheus, who was tortured eternally for having stolen the heavenly fire from Zeus. This vulture gnawing at the hearts of men was remorse. 'Scientists are bewildered and frustrated,' wrote *Time*. 'Most of them do not know where they are. The bomb has shattered their cloistered world as effectively as it reduced Hiroshima to ruins. They haunt the ruins of their own world, like disconsolate or enraged ghosts.'

Even before the fatal day in 1945, a few of the great names in nuclear physics – Bohr, Einstein, Rabinowitch – had opposed the use of the bomb. They had at first tried to keep the secret of the atom, then had given it to the Allies at war, and in the end were shattered by it all. These 'titans', these 'devilish gods', as Jungk called them, started a desperate campaign; they held protest meetings, and formed the 'Federation of American Scientists'; they endeavoured to persuade men everywhere of the urgent necessity to place atomic energy under international control, to be applied only for peaceful purposes and the benefit of mankind. Scientists left Los Alamos by the hundreds, perhaps in the hope of depriving the military of the secret that had slipped from their grasp. All this confusion in thought and act made the wily old politicians smile quietly to themselves – whatever those infantile scientists did, they were sure to get completely lost in the maze of world politics. The corridors of Congress and the halls of the United Nations were different from laboratories. And General Groves, looking at the deserted buildings of Los Alamos, confidently predicted: 'They'll come back!'

And come back they did, after a short time.

The crusade against atomic weapons, the 'League of Horrified Men' as it was called, met with one bitter setback after another. The scientists made contacts in the Soviet Union, but that country was too occupied with the making of its own bomb to do more

[1] Copyright 1948, Christian Century Foundation. Reprinted by permission from the June 16, 1948 issue of *The Christian Century*.

than listen with half an ear. For the chill of the cold war was already in the air ... Many of the younger generation of scientists had no scruples in carrying on the work, feeling no direct responsibility for the first A-bomb. Moreover, these men had been trained in America, where anything that seems possible is soon carried out. The older standards of Western civilization, its humanity, ideals and dialectic, had very little meaning for them.

The scientists of the older generation, those educated in the traditions of Göttingen, Heidelberg or Vienna, felt powerless. Some were fortunate enough to be able to return to their peacetime laboratories. Dr Kenneth Bainbridge, for instance, had a huge cyclotron costing four hundred thousand dollars built for him at Harvard. But the Army was pouring millions of dollars into the universities, hoping to reap rewards sooner or later. And politicians did their best to stifle the consciences of research-workers.

The most striking instance was brought to the public notice in 1954 when Robert Oppenheimer appeared before the Atomic Energy Commission. Oppenheimer had given his country the atomic bomb, he had rallied round him all the scientific brains in America, and yet by a strange blow of fate it was he who became the first victim of wild allegations. He was accused of having been a Communist, of having systematically opposed the hydrogen bomb project, and of being disloyal to his country. And through him the McCarthy witch-hunters were implicating the whole of the modern scientific world. It had heedlessly bound itself to the military juggernaut, and had yielded up its freedom.

In Russia, the wrath of the country's leaders fell upon the head of Piotr Kapitza. In 1946 he had made an appeal to the physicists of the world to combine against the atomic peril. His appeal got as far as the ears of the men in the Kremlin, and they had him thrown into prison, where he remained for seven years. Other Soviet scientists were dealt with even more harshly, being sent to labour camps for indefinite periods. The rest did as they were told, through patriotism or prudence; and the first Russian atomic bomb was exploded in Central Asia in August 1949.

Otto Hahn, the scientist who had first split the atom, contemplated suicide when he realized what use had been made of his work. Some of the Los Alamos scientists deeply regretted having been involved in the Manhattan Project. 'If we had known that

Hitler did not possess the bomb, we would never have helped to make one,' they proclaimed, many years later. They could see no end to their remorse. But it was a very different matter with the Peenemünde scientists.

One wonders exactly how many of them really regretted making weapons for Hitler, though they probably deplored the fact, long afterwards, that their master had *used* these arms. But as Von Braun said: 'If I hadn't done it, someone else would.' One of his colleagues went further: 'What we wanted to do was to build space-craft. The way necessarily went through military fields.'

Far from regretting having worked at Kummersdorf and Peenemünde, the German scientists were proud of it; they had become legendary figures, knights of science. In any case, their American masters played down the strategic importance of Hitler's V.1s and V.2s, and emphasized the 'space' aspect of the research that these men had carried out on the shores of the Baltic. The Germans were naturally not slow to seize on this means of justifying their actions. Nevertheless, one of Von Braun's colleagues said to an American journalist: 'Don't kid yourself, Von Braun might have been obsessed by space travel since his childhood, but it doesn't alter the fact that we were all greatly influenced by the Allied air-raids on Germany. When the first V.2 struck London, the champagne flowed at Peenemünde. Let's be honest – we were at war, and although we weren't Nazis we had to defend our country.'

How is it possible to explain the clear consciences of those who built deadly rockets, long-range submarines or swift aircraft, and the anguished remorse of the atomic scientists? The explanation may be that the former were engineers with their feet firmly on the ground; whereas the atomic scientists were isolated in their ivory towers, lost in the intoxication of pure research, and when they emerged from their dream-world they found that they had destroyed the world in which they could have worked so peacefully.

The German scientists turned more and more to an excuse which fitted the trend of international politics. Hellmut Walter, for example, said: 'We had realized, long before anyone else, what a menace the Soviet Union was to Western civilization and culture. And that is why we helped Hitler.'

One of the officers who had been in charge of the 'paperclip boys' at Fort Bliss, Colonel Sestito, once explained to a journalist the scientific mercenaries' manner of thinking: 'Actually, their political attitude to their work seems to spring from a syllogism which Goebbels might have propounded. That is, Germans have always led the way in Western culture, the United States has undertaken the defense of Western culture against the Russians, therefore the United States is defending German culture.'

However, the German scientists who had been on the other side of the Iron Curtain followed another line of argument: 'We tried to defend the West against the Soviet menace; but the Russians won and the future is theirs. So it is quite reasonable and logical to put ourselves at their service.'

But those German scientists found it impossible to become assimilated with the Russian people; they were rejected as a foreign body. It is true that they received compensation in the form of Stalin Prizes and the Order of Lenin ... What truth was there in the rumor that Russia was the Promised Land for scientists? In any case, such a belief led to the growth of a new category of scientists. Following the scientific mercenaries came the scientific spies.

Klaus Fuchs and Others

'A man is arriving from England to work in New York with a group of American scientists. He will have information about an entirely new, devastating weapon. Contact him as soon as he arrives and try to get as much as possible out of him.'

According to a journalist, Sanche de Gramont, those were the instructions that the Russian master-spy, Sam Semenov, sent to Harry Gold, the trusted Russian agent in New York. Gold received this message early in 1944, and it was the beginning of the most extraordinary scientific spy story of the century.

Sanche de Gramont's account goes on to describe the meeting with the man from England, whose name was unknown to Gold. It took place in February 1944, in a deserted district on the East Side of New York where slums were being demolished to make way for huge apartment blocks. The stranger was a tall, thin man with a pallid face; he was wearing dark glasses and ostentatiously holding a tennis ball in his hand. As a mark of recognition, Gold

G

was wearing gloves and carrying a second pair and had a book under his arm.

The two walked away together, without exchanging a word, and when they reached the centre of the city they went into a restaurant, the 'Manny Wolf'. There, the man with the dark glasses introduced himself. 'I'm working with a group of scientists, over near Wall Street. We are engaged on the Manhattan Project. My name is Klaus Fuchs.'

Six years later almost to the day, on 27 January 1950, Klaus Fuchs stepped from a train in a London station, where a stout man greeted him politely and took him to a waiting car. They got out in Whitehall, and when they were alone in an office Fuchs's companion broke the silence. 'Are you ready to make a statement?' And for some hours, Inspector James William Skardon of Scotland Yard listened to the scientist.

'I am a research scientist at the Harwell Atomic Energy Establishment,' Fuchs began. 'I was born on 29 December 1911, at Rüsselheim; and my father was a pastor. I had a happy childhood.'

'At the beginning I thought I only had to keep the Russians informed of the progress being made on the American atomic bomb,' Fuchs continued in a calm, steady voice. 'But later, especially when I was at Los Alamos, I committed what I consider to be my most shameful action. I communicated the report on the principle of the construction of the plutonium bomb. My last message to the Russians was in 1949, in February or March ...'

And he went on, in the same flat, monotonous voice, to disclose all the ramifications of this great spy ring to the impassive Skardon.

Fuchs had come to Britain in 1934, fleeing from Hitler, and worked in Edinburgh with the famous physicist Max Born. When war broke out he was sent to an internment camp in Canada with other 'enemy aliens'. In the spring of 1941 he was brought back to England, as Rudolf Peierls had asked for his collaboration on a 'special project'. Fuchs thus joined the small group of physicists engaged on the 'Tube Alloys' program, the innocent-sounding name given to the British atomic project.

In August, 1942, after he had successfully carried out experiments on the separation of uranium, Fuchs received his British naturalisation papers. By this time, he had certainly earned an equal claim to Soviet citizenship.

As soon as he found out what was behind 'Tube Alloys' he made contact with British Communists. A Communist himself, he believed he had a humanitarian mission – for the future safety of mankind, the Anglo-American bomb had to be counter-balanced by a Russian bomb.

British Communists put him in touch with Russian secret agents; and he left his office more and more frequently with papers and documents in his pockets. He used to meet a certain Simon Kramer, who was later replaced by a woman, and each time he reached home his pockets were empty.

In November 1943, Fuchs went to the United States with a small group of outstanding atomic scientists. Once he became engaged on the Manhattan Project he began passing Harry Gold thick wads of paper covered with his tiny, compact writing. He noted down on the sheets of paper everything he knew – the work being carried out at Columbia University, and all the details of the nuclear research at Oak Ridge. In January 1945, Fuchs met Gold at Cambridge, Massachusetts, and gave him a report which mentioned for the first time the forbidden city of Los Alamos. At four in the afternoon of 2 June 1945, they met on the Castillo bridge at Santa Fe, only twenty miles from Los Alamos; and Gold received a hundred or so sheets of notes which Fuchs had written out late at night. This information was not only about a forthcoming test, but described the mechanism of the two atomic bombs, indicated that one was a uranium bomb and the other plutonium, and furthermore revealed the research being done on a thermo-nuclear bomb – the even more terrible H-bomb.

Fuchs returned to Britain a year later, with the firm intention of leading a quiet life, merely passing a few scraps of information to the Russians if this should prove necessary. But his arrest early in 1950 put an end to this peaceful existence. Once he was caught, he decided to make a clean breast of it all.

His confession had great repercussions in government circles of the Western powers. When President Truman heard of it, he recalled a strange incident at the Potsdam meeting. He had leaned across to Stalin and whispered that the United States possessed the most powerful bomb ever known and that it was soon to be dropped on Japan to force her to surrender. But Stalin had shown no surprise at this sensational piece of information. 'I'm glad to hear of it,' he said almost casually. 'I hope that you will at least make use of this bomb . . .'

In the light of Fuchs's confession, President Truman understood why Stalin had shown no surprise. The Russian leader already had accurate information on the Manhattan Project.

Fuchs sincerely believed that by bringing about a balance between the nuclear powers the world could be saved from disaster. Another scientist with similar ideas was Professor Alan Nunn May. He was arrested by plain-clothes detectives on 4 March 1946, as he was leaving King's College, London. He, too, had worked at Harwell, and during the war had been at the head of a group of physicists sent to work on the Anglo-Canadian atomic project at Chalk River. The Russians only knew of this eminent scientist as 'Alec', one of their most valued agents. He had supplied them with long reports on the bomb, and had even sent them precious samples of uranium 233 and 235.

The young Italian physicist, Bruno Pontecorvo, who had been Enrico Fermi's favorite student, may also have had the same humanitarian impulse, although some of his colleagues, who were probably jealous of his popularity with women, said that he had no moral sense at all. In any case, throughout the war Pontecorvo was continually travelling between the American and Canadian atomic establishments, and at the same time was supplying the Russians with copious scientific information. In 1950 he suddenly disappeared behind the Iron Curtain to take refuge in Russia.

Whether they were humanitarians or Communists, penitent or content, unmasked or still unsuspected, these scientific spies were nevertheless trump-cards in the Soviet hand. Some of these men were perhaps only visionaries, convinced that scientific research knew no frontiers and that the petty quarrels of ordinary men ought not to have any unpleasant consequences for the great international brotherhood of supermen.

'Would you have helped the Russians if they had contacted you during the war?' one of the Los Alamos scientists was asked.

'Perhaps I should have done,' he answered candidly. 'You know, we scientists don't easily accept rigid conventions or preconceived ideas. We always keep an open mind. We're ready to listen and learn, and to be convinced by right ideas. If the Russians had been able to persuade me that by helping them I should be doing useful work – well, you know, I shouldn't have refused.'

It was to show they had 'an open mind' that the 'League of Horrified Men' had tried to get international control of nuclear research. The reasoning of the scientists was most debatable, but it was a clear indication of their confusion and bewilderment.

This was the factor with which the scientist-hunters of the cold war had to contend. It was obviously the Russians who were going to draw most benefit from the troubled consciences of the atomic scientists. Back in 1943 they had discreetly sounded Oppenheimer, through the intermediary of Charles Eltenton and Haakon Chevalier; but he had shown no inclination to cooperate, and the Russians had cast their net elsewhere.

The Soviet purchasing commission in the United States became an active center of espionage, and agents succeeded in obtaining large quantities of uranium as well as documents of scientific importance. Alger Hiss, a high official in the State Department, was tried and found guilty of working for the Russians. The Rosenberg couple paid with their lives for having belonged to a spy-ring whose activities were linked with those of Harry Gold, David Greenglass, Morton Sobel and Alfred Dean Slack.

The master-spies, Rudolf Abel and Gordon Lansdale, succeeded in persuading American and British scientists to reveal their secrets to save the peace of the world. Eugenio Chavez, an amiable hairdresser who attended to the German scientists working at White Sands, New Mexico, was found to be a spy interested in guided missiles.

In Britain, members of a spy-ring interested in the nuclear submarine *Dreadnought* were arrested at Portland. While in Russia, Colonel Oleg Penkovski, a hero of the Second World War, was executed by firing-squad for having betrayed military and scientific secrets of his country to Britain.

Scientists were thus made aware that they could no longer take shelter in an ivory tower. The weapons of war were now rocket missiles, atomic bombs, nuclear submarines and earth satellites; and scientists everywhere had become vulnerable. They were followed and watched, and their private lives were probed into; they were hidden away behind curtains of iron, bamboo or sand, but sometimes a well-concealed microphone was sufficient to single them out for destruction – as was proved by one of the most astounding episodes in this secret, merciless war of espionage.

CHAPTER THIRTEEN

Nasser Employs Some Germans

A New Man-Hunt

Shrove Tuesday, 1963 ... and in Zurich, the Carnival was at its height. Some two thousand artists, sculptors and musicians had gathered in the gaily decorated Kongress Haus, the restaurant on the lakeside, for the traditional masked ball. In all the crush and bustle, nobody paid any attention to a dozen men in ordinary clothes who had come in through different doors and were mingling with the crowd. These intruders, members of the Zurich police, were keeping close watch on two men who were still in the bar– a heavy man wearing dark glasses and a Tyrolean hat, and his companion, who had a fair moustache.

The previous day the police in Freiberg, Germany, had received a report that a young woman in the town was being threatened by some foreign agents. She had agreed to meet them at four the following afternoon at the Three Kings Hotel in Basel, Switzerland. The Swiss police had been asked to take over.

A fortnight earlier, Heidi Goerke, a twenty-five-year-old woman barrister in Freiburg and the daughter of a well-known scientist, Paul Goerke, had had a visit from a certain Otto Frank Joklik, an Austrian. He had said he knew her father, who was working in Cairo for the Egyptian Government. Professor Goerke, continued Joklik, was making fearful weapons with which Egypt intended to destroy the young State of Israel. And Joklik impressed upon the young woman the necessity for her to persuade her father to abandon this dangerous work – otherwise something serious, most serious, might happen to the scientist and his family.

A few days after this meeting, Heidi Goerke had a telephone call from Joklik. 'If you value your father's safety,' he said, 'meet me at four o'clock on Saturday afternoon, the second of March, at the Three Kings Hotel in Basle. I want you to meet a friend of mine.'

Heidi Goerke informed the West German police of these threats. She was told to keep the rendezvous in Basle; and was assured that the Swiss police would see to her safety and check on the two men.

So on the afternoon of 2 March, Heidi Goerke was waiting in the hotel at Basle, sitting at a side table in the lounge with her young brother; in a wall lamp above the table, a tiny microphone had been installed. A number of men were sitting in armchairs about the lounge, trying to be inconspicuous behind opened newspapers. A journalist who had got wind of the affair and wanted to be present was told to keep away, 'as there may be shooting'. In the street, several police cars were ready for any emergency. The trap had been set; it remained to be seen whether the two secret agents would walk into it.

Joklik's friend, the man with a fair moustache, had been followed as soon as he crossed the frontier into Switzerland. He wandered through the streets of Basle for a time, went into a café and made a telephone call, then walked to the hotel. He may have become suspicious, for he said very little throughout the meeting, merely stating that he was an Israeli and making a few allusions to Professor Goerke's dangerous situation. Joklik, who had been the first to arrive, did most of the talking.

Heidi Goerke gave the two men no definite answer. The men left the hotel – still followed by the police – and went to the station, where they caught the six o'clock train to Zurich. The police there were ready for them, but took no immediate action. The two were seen to enter the lakeside Kongress Haus, scene of the artists' ball, and go to the bar. If they happened to don masks and try to mingle with the crowd of dancers, the police were ready for them.

But they left after having a drink, and parted outside the flood-lit restaurant. The Israeli strolled along the lake shore in the direction of his country's Consulate. The Swiss police caught up with him just before he reached it. 'May we see your passport?' The document he produced was in the name of Joseph Ben-Gal, an official at the Ministry of Education, and seemed quite in order. Nevertheless, the police asked him to go with them. At about the same time, Joklik was being arrested at the railway station.

The two were questioned at length, but their arrest was not announced until a fortnight later. On 15 March, the Swiss authorities issued a statement that two foreign agents were being charged with making threats against the person of Heidi Goerke.

This brought into the open the controversy of the German scientists in Egypt.

Tel Aviv on the Warpath

Sensational headlines in the world's press: 'German scientists in Egypt making forbidden weapons' – 'Nazi scientists making A B C weapons (atomic, bacteriological, chemical) for Nasser' – 'Nasser's secret weapon is the death ray.' Press comment was equally pungent: 'Israel has denounced the German scientists who are helping to make an Egyptian deterrent ... The Israelis have good reasons for kidnapping the German scientists ... It is a matter of life and death for Israel ... Tel Aviv is on the warpath against the Germans working for Nasser.'

Tel Aviv was indeed on the warpath. A campaign had been launched to draw world attention to the activities of German scientists which threatened the small Jewish State. The Israeli Minister for Foreign Affairs, Mrs Golda Meir, had sharply requested the Bonn Government to recall the German 'brains' at work in Egypt. In reply, the Federal Republic expressed disapproval of their activities, but pointed out with some embarrassment that it had no legal means of curtailing them.

What were these activities? They must have constituted a serious menace, because for the first time since Suez all the Israeli political parties were united.

Some fantastic stories had been published. The long list of horrible scientific weapons included the death ray, shells filled with deadly bacteria, poison gas and radioactive waste. Names were mentioned, addresses given, and the position of secret bases and factories divulged. The number of German scientists in Egypt was variously given, and there was rumored to be an underground criminal organization with connections extending from Egypt to Switzerland and even to India.

What truth was there in all this? Were the Germans in Egypt common mercenaries and ex-Nazis, and how long had they been there?

The answer was in the files of the Israeli secret service, beginning with the clipping of an advertisement which had appeared in several German newspapers in 1958: 'Aeronautical industry in North Africa requires specialists ...'

The Advisers

It had all started during the immediate post-war years, when German army officers whose Nazi record made it advisable for them to leave Europe had tried their luck in Cairo. Some of them found positions as 'technical advisers' to the Egyptian Army. Their numbers steadily grew. Ex-officers of the Afrika Korps, inspectors lately in the Gestapo, young disciples of Goebbels, they had wandered about the world for a time, from Spain to Argentina, before finding a haven by the sun-drenched banks of the Nile. For greater convenience, some of them had changed their names. SS Lieutenant Ulrich Kraus became Mohamed Akbar, his colleagues Achim Dieter Peschnik and Adolf Putsbeck became, respectively, El Said and Ben Outsien, while Gerd von Nimzek took the simple name of Ben Ali. Egyptians surprised at the bad Arabic spoken by Mohamed Assein would have understood the reason had they known that he was really Jurgen Knetch, one-time head of Nazi propaganda in Montevideo and lately a senior officer in the crack Das Reich division.

Another batch of arrivals in Cairo included Leopold Gleim, who had been head of the Gestapo in Warsaw and had a death sentence hanging over his head; SS General Oscar Dirlewanger and Willi Brenner, who had organized the Mauthausen concentration camp. The group was headed by Von Leers, one of Goebbels's chief assistants; he went to live in a villa in Meadi, a residential suburb of Cairo.

It was not until 1951, however, that the German colony came into its own. That year, General Wilhelm Fahrmbacher, an artillery specialist, arrived in Egypt with about forty ex-army officers. They were appointed to different branches of the Egyptian Army, and did such good work that after the overthrow of King Farouk in 1952 the army clique which seized power rewarded them with promotions and greater responsibilities.

An officer who had been on General Guderian's staff was made adviser to the armored brigade. Germans who had been in command of paratroops, of frogmen or of commandos were placed in charge of recruits in the Egyptian armed forces. Three ex-Hitler Youth leaders began to organize youth movements. Some fifteen German test-pilots and specialists in jet-planes replaced British experts at the De Havilland assembly factories. German technicians joined the army research centres and the ordnance factories, and the ballistics section of the Helouan munition works; their salaries were not very high – about seventy pounds a month – and they were poorly housed just outside Heliopolis.

The popular meeting-place of the Germans was the Brewery Löwenbrau on 26th July Street in Cairo, where more and more clients were seen lifting their glasses of beer to toasts of 'Prosit!'

A few months before Farouk fell, there arrived in Cairo a German who had had an important position with the Hermann Goering munition works and had also been manager of the Skoda works in Czechoslovakia during the German occupation. He was Dr Wilhelm Voss, and after the revolt against Farouk the military leaders asked him to take charge of the production of small-calibre rockets. Voss went hunting for scientists, and in Paris he unearthed Rolf Engel, who was then working for the French at the National Office of Aeronautical Research. Voss offered to put him in charge of the CERVA, the Egyptian company which was to make the tactical rockets. Engel accepted, and left for Cairo to start work. Voss, meanwhile, remained in France recruiting research workers for his team – including Professor Paul Goerke, an electronics expert who had been at Peenemünde.

Goerke had been employed in France on the Véronique rocket. In Egypt, at Heliopolis, he went to work on radar. But in 1954 he returned to Europe. Voss went back to Germany in 1956 – the year of Suez. In 1957 the military junta which was running Egypt had to abandon the idea of equipping the army with tactical rockets; the CERVA had ceased to exist. Rolf Engel left Egypt and took a job in Italy. Many other German specialists, General Fahrmbacher among them, took ship at Alexandria during 1958; and the following year the last of the team, Colonel

Beierlein, who had been Rommel's aide-de-camp, left Egyptian shores.

A Help Wanted Ad

When Nasser came to power he set about building up an armaments industry to provide Egypt with jet planes and powerful rocket weapons. He knew from experience that the Israeli army was far superior to the Egyptian in conventional weapons. The Israeli Air Force was equipped with the most modern planes, and the Egyptians needed even faster ones; Russia could supply them, but the price she demanded – a political alignment – was much too high. In a future war against Israel the Egyptians might well be beaten in the field, but they had to be able to inflict heavy losses on the enemy's communications and rear. And to this end, Egypt had to build up her own powerful air force and, especially, produce rocket-missiles.

So the famous 'help wanted' ad appeared in a number of German newspapers. At the same time, some hand-picked teams of Egyptians left for Europe to go hunting after scientists on their own.

One of the first replies to the advertisement, sent to a Zurich box number, came from Ferdinand Brandner. He, as already mentioned, had been freed by the Russians in 1954 after having built 'the most powerful aero-engines in the world' for them. Since then he had been trying to find employment in the European aircraft industry, but the fact that he was an ex-SS colonel had gone against him; a recent application to a company in the Federal Republic which had NATO contracts had been unsuccessful.

Brandner had aged a lot but was still full of ideas. He readily accepted the propositions made to him by one of Nasser's agents, a somewhat mysterious individual with the name of Hassan Kamil, who said he was a Swiss industrialist of Egyptian origin. Brandner went round visiting the aviation works in Germany and Austria, and the technical institutes from Aix-la-Chapelle to Graz, recruiting old colleagues who had worked with him at Dessau or Kuybyshev. He had much to offer them – attractive salaries, possibilities of doing research work, and the lovely Mediterranean sunshine. Before long, he had two hundred names on his list of acceptants.

The Egyptians, in the meantime, had not been idle; they had discovered another recruiting agent with many connections – Willy Messerschmitt. His plants in the Federal Republic were building jet-planes for NATO; he had interests in Spain, and was connected with many Austrian and Swiss firms. His name alone was a drawing card.

On 29 November 1959, the contracts between Messerschmitt and the Egyptian government were signed in a private house in Munich. Nasser's representative was a stout man of about fifty with wavy hair and a long, drooping moustache – Aldin Mahmoud Khalil. He had been head of Intelligence in the Egyptian Air Force, and was soon to have charge of the 'special military projects' and to have great influence with Nasser. The German scientists called him 'Herr Doktor Mahmoud'.

However, while glasses were being raised to the newly signed agreement and the German signatories pocketed a cheque for one hundred thousand Egyptian pounds, teams of scientist-hunters were busy all over Germany. The time was right for the hunt, because game was abundant in 1959 and 1960. The last of the German scientists had been sent home from the Black Sea resort of Soukhoumi, and many others were back from Britain, France and the United States. They were all itching to build jet-engines, to discover a new rocket-fuel or to send rockets soaring away for thousands of miles – amusements which were forbidden to them in their fatherland.

The Egyptians were well aware of all this. They combed the technical colleges and research institutes where many scientists had found places (which did not satisfy their ambitions); then the hunters headed for Bavaria, with a stopover at the Jet-Propulsion Study Institute in Stuttgart, where the director of studies was known to be Eugen Sänger.

The 'Choir-Boys'

Sänger, who had been hunted once before, by the Russians, was a bitterly disappointed man. In both Russia and America, scientists were pursuing a project based on an idea of his, but the work was being done without him. Sänger had always been fifty years in advance of his time, and now he was doing very little scientific work while others were launching Sputniks or Explorers.

The rocket research in which he had been engaged in France had proved to be of limited importance, and in 1954 he returned to Germany to take up a teaching post in Stuttgart. He founded an international federation of associations for rocket research, and he was awarded the Hermann Oberth medal; he published articles on space travel now and again, but his name was gradually sinking into oblivion. Not surprisingly, therefore, he jumped at the Egyptians' invitation to take charge of their 'forbidden city'. 'Shall I be able to build a rocket to launch an earth satellite?' he asked. 'Why not?' they said, for they were ready to promise anything in order to have his services.

In addition to Sänger, the Egyptian scientist-hunters came upon the three scientists who had worked in France on the Véronique rocket. They were Wolfgang Pilz, Goerke – who had already spent a year in Egypt – and Kleinwachter. The French had not treated Pilz with the consideration he believed to be his due, and since he had been poorly paid and housed he did not look back with pleasure upon the time spent at Châtillon. The French had never shown any tender feelings towards the late enemy 'brains'. 'They lost the war, now let them work for us,' was the attitude. But Pilz was still discontented after returning to Germany. He proposed a rocket-missile project to the Bonn authorities, one on the lines of the British 'Blue Streak', but it was turned down. Thus, another bitterly disappointed man, he readily accepted the Egyptian offer.

As for Goerke, he had happy memories of his stay in Egypt and agreed to go back. Kleinwachter had signed a contract and put his private laboratory at the disposal of the Egyptians.

The German scientists arrived in Cairo, in the greatest secrecy, in 1960. Each of the principals had brought with him as many technicians and engineers as possible, and the Brewery Löwenbrau was hardly big enough to hold all the Germans. Brandner had with him a tall, fair-haired engineer named Naye, and also Waldemar Schierhorn, who had spent many years in Egypt. Willy Messerschmitt had fifteen engineers headed by Fritz Hentzen and Spiess, while Sänger was accompanied by an enthusiastic group of youngsters from the Stuttgart Institute. These technicians, fresh from the classroom, soon became known as *Sänger Knaben* – a play on words in German, meaning either 'Sänger's boys' or 'choir-boys'.

36, 135, 333

These figures concealed the secrets of Nasser's wonder weapons.

'36' denoted the white factory just outside Cairo where the fuselages for supersonic aircraft were being built. Messerschmitt was at the head of it.

'135' was Brandner's domain, twenty miles outside the capital. The tall buildings with their many windows ended in hangars and wind-tunnels for the testing of aero-engines. In the workshops, the safety notices were in Arabic and German.

'333' was the rocket establishment out in the desert, not far from Heliopolis; it was surrounded by barbed wire and machine-gun posts. The few Egyptians who knew of these secret installations called them the *Thalathat* – the 'Threes'. A score of Germans worked there under the three departmental heads, Pilz, Goerke and Schuran.

The whole project was controlled from Cairo by 'Herr Doktor Mahmoud', who reported directly to Nasser. The chief objectives of the 'special military projects' had been settled early in 1960 – the construction of the He.200, a trainer-fighter, and the He. 300, a supersonic fighter-plane of international class. The latter, which was to have a bullet-shaped nose, had been designed some time before by Messerschmitt's assistants, but there was no possibility of building it in Germany or at the works in Spain.

As for the rocket programme, two types were envisaged – a small tactical rocket and a long-range one. Sänger and Pilz had brought the plans with them in their briefcases.

Egypt had her cotton and her gold, foreign currencies and the German scientists, but she still lacked one thing to carry out her projects. She had no aircraft-component industry. And foreign firms would probably refuse to supply Egypt with material and apparatus intended for military purposes if pressure were put upon them by their governments, as seemed more than likely.

However, there were ways round these difficulties. The Egyptians opened offices and agencies abroad to buy patents and to manufacture needed apparatus. In Munich, an inoffensive company known by its initial letters as INTRA bought the rights on a number of foreign patents relating to rocket-motors and their electrical apparatus. The company was in the names of Pilz and Goerke, and its manager was an ex-army officer, Dr Heinz Krug. In Zurich, the MECO had close dealings with the Spanish branch of the Messerschmitt works. Another Swiss company, the MTP (Motors, Turbines and Pumps) handled jet-engines, in collaboration with INTRA in Munich. Both the Swiss companies were in the name of Hassan Kamil, the man who had contacted Brandner and others. A code was used in communications with headquarters in Cairo, and the word 'button' kept appearing – red or green buttons, copper or iron buttons – to refer to engine parts, gyroscopes or important people.

Krug and Kamil, sometimes assisted by experts who had come specially from Egypt (such as Schierhorn, Kleinwachter, Brandner), arranged for the despatch of a great quantity of the needed material to Cairo. Messerschmitt obtained some ejectable seats and a few French aero-engines for the early tests. But his most important contribution was to obtain the cooperation of Kurt Tank.

After the fall of Peron, Tank had left Argentina and returned to Germany with a dozen other scientific brains. He tried to interest the Bonn Government in his projects, but despite the support of the prime minister of Schleswig-Holstein, Von Hassel (later the Federal Republic's Defence Minister), Tank was unsuccessful and decided once again to seek work abroad. He went to India; and eventually built, at Bangalore, the first Indian jet-fighter, the Hindustan or HF. 24, which was fitted with British 'Orpheus' engines.

Brandner was making slow progress with his supersonic fighter, the He.300, and 'Herr Doktor Mahmoud' was becoming impatient. So Brandner had one of his bright ideas. If the engines to be used for the He.300 could be tested in flight, much time would be saved. Suppose that Tank lent a Hindustan for the purpose? Brandner could take out one of the 'Orpheus' engines and replace it with his own; if that failed during flight, the other 'Orpheus' would enable the plane to land safely. And if all went well, Tank could be asked to fit the Egyptian engines into his fighters instead of the British 'Orpheus'. The links between Egypt and India would thus be strengthened.

Tank agreed to cooperate in this way. So the scientists who

had served Hitler, then Stalin and Peron, were about to serve the cause of practical neutralism!

The Israeli 'Comet'

Nasser's policy of practical neutralism called for socialist austerity on the part of the Egyptian people, but he allowed the German scientists a few exceptions to the rule. The lowest salary any German received was about three hundred pounds a month. A chief engineer was paid as much as seven hundred and fifty pounds, or nearly two thousand five hundred dollars, a month. Many of the Germans had been given luxurious, air-conditioned houses at Heliopolis and Meadi. Their handsome sports-cars were often seen at the Heliopolis Sporting Club, where the swimming-pool always seemed full of Germans. They organized a 'Rhineland Carnival' at the Hilton Hotel; and a whole floor at Shepheard's was reserved for Willy Messerschmitt, who went to Cairo once a month. Pilz and Kleinwachter liked to go for long rides in the desert or to fish in the Red Sea.

However, the work did not suffer from these luxurious indulgences. The rocket program was well advanced; and the first He.200, the trainer-fighter, freshly painted in the Egyptian colors, took part in the military display on 26 July, the anniversary of the revolt against Farouk. But there was a cloud on the Egyptian horizon. Israel had just successfully launched her first solid-fuel rocket-missile, called the Shavit (Comet) Two. As an Israeli staff officer explained: 'That will give Nasser plenty to think about. By calling our first rocket Shavit Two we shall make him wonder what happened to Shavit One.'

Whatever its real number, the rocket made the Egyptians very anxious. According to information they received, it had reached a height of fifty miles, leaving a brilliant cloud of sodium behind. Mahmoud showed Sänger some pictures of it. 'What do you think that is?' he asked. 'Only a weather rocket,' the German replied. 'Weather rocket or not, start working faster,' said the other. 'We can't let ourselves be left behind.'

But things began to go wrong with the Egyptians' plans. At the beginning of 1962 Messerschmitt recommended the dismissal of several chief scientists at the '36' factory, because he had noticed faults in the fuselages being built for He.200s and 300s. Mahmoud approved, especially as Messerschmitt had men to replace the dismissed scientists. An Austrian, Dr Schoenbaumfeld, took over the factory from Dr Hentzen, and a specialist from the Siebel works, Dr Stang, replaced Spiess, the chief engineer. Fifteen Germans in all were told to leave Egypt, although their contracts had not expired. They did not hide their wrath, and threatened to bring an action against the United Arab Republic.

Nasser's Rocket-Missiles

An even more serious crisis was affecting the rocket program. At the end of 1961 Sänger had been forced to resign and to return to Germany.

Israeli secret agents had discovered an unusual coming and going between Cairo and the Stuttgart Institute. They had followed the activities of the undercover firms in Germany and Switzerland; they had also built up a list of the scientists working for Nasser, and had made detailed maps of the positions of the secret Egyptian factories. Armed with this damning evidence, Tel Aviv made approaches to Bonn.

The Federal Republic was at least able to put pressure on the Stuttgart research workers who had gone to work for the Egyptians, as the Institute was subsidized by the government. Bonn declared all the contracts void and ordered Sânger to return to Germany. He submitted and was appointed head of an aviation study-center in West Berlin.

This was a great loss for the 'Threes' rocket establishment. But Sänger's senior colleagues preferred to stay where they were and abandon their functions in Germany. Pilz took Sänger's place as head of the 'forbidden city', and Schuran became chief of the rocket-motor department.

It could be said that nothing had really changed. But as the Bonn Defense Minister, F. J. Strauss, dryly commented: 'It remains to be seen who profited most – Nasser from Sänger, or Sänger from Nasser.'

An answer was provided on 26 July 1962, when a triumphant Nasser, accompanied by a throng of journalists, watched the successful launching of two rockets, one large and the other small, and both painted black and white. The highlight of the military procession was the dozens of big rockets draped with the

Egyptian flag which were carried on trailers and guarded by soldiers standing at attention. The crowds of spectators applauded them wildly all along the route. An official communiqué issued on this great day announced that Egypt possessed two new rocket-missiles– 'Al Zafir' (The Victor), which had a range of one hundred and seventy-five miles, and 'Al Kahir' (The Conqueror), with a range of three hundred and fifty miles. The latter, as Nasser did not fail to point out, was capable of reaching any objective south of Beirut.

South of Beirut! At Tel Aviv the communiqué was regarded as almost equivalent to a declaration of war – a war that the Israeli secret services began to pursue against the German scientists.

Who Was Sending the Time-Bombs?

One day in July 1962, Hassan Kamil, the mysterious Swiss industrialist who was running the MECO and MTP offices, chartered a plane to take him and his wife from the island of Sylt to Düsseldorf. At the last moment he found himself obliged to remain on the island for a day or two longer, so his German wife flew to Düsseldorf without him. A few hours later, news came that the plane had crashed in Westphalia and its pilot and passenger had both been killed. Was it an accident, or had an attempt been made on Kamil's life?

At half-past ten on the morning of 10 September a dark-skinned man with oriental features entered the INTRA office in Schillerstrasse, Munich. When he left a little later he was accompanied by the manager, Heinz Krug. An air-hostess in the United Arab Airlines office saw the two pass the window, and after that all trace of Krug was lost. His wife telephoned to the police the following day to report him missing.

Two days later Krug's car, which had disappeared from its garage, was found not far from town spattered with mud, with its petrol-tank empty. The police received an anonymous telephone call to say that Dr Krug was dead. But there were rumors that he had been kidnapped by an Israeli commando, or by a gang that had sold him to Israel for the handsome price of seventy thousand pounds sterling.

On the morning of 27 November, Pilz's secretary, Hannelore

Wende, was opening the mail in his office at the 'Threes'. It included a large parcel which, according to the return address, came from a well-known barrister in Hamburg. The young woman opened the parcel – and the office was shaken by a loud explosion. She was badly injured about the face, and spent many months in a Cairo hospital. Who could have sent this time-bomb?

On 28 November another large parcel was delivered at the 'Threes', this time to the general office. It had come by sea from Hamburg, and was marked 'specialized literature'. An Egyptian civil servant tore open the parcel, and it exploded, killing five people. An enquiry found that the name of a Stuttgart bookshop on the parcel was false.

The following day two parcels were delivered, both having the same markings and label as the previous parcel. Profiting by experience, the Egyptian authorities had them examined by experts, who found that each parcel contained books filled with explosives. No statement was made as to the possible identity of the senders; but rumors said that the Israelis, with a touch of grim humor, were calling the parcels 'Post Mortem'.

On 23 February, 1963, Dr Hans Kleinwachter – who had gone to Germany for a few weeks – got into his car outside his laboratory in Lörrach to drive home. As he turned into the lane leading to his house, another car cut across him and braked sharply, forcing him to stop. It was a lonely spot, and there was snow on the ground. A man got out of the car and walked towards Kleinwachter. In his driving-mirror he could see there were two other men in the car. The third man said to him 'Where does Dr Schenker live?' But without waiting for a reply he drew a revolver equipped with a silencer, and fired. The bullet shattered the windscreen and lodged in the scientist's muffler; he groped for his own revolver, which he kept under the dashboard. But the man ran back to the other car, which was promptly driven off.

The police were informed, and later they discovered the car abandoned only a few hundred yards from the scene of the attack. The three men had made their escape in another car. They left a passport behind, in the name of Ali Samir, who was one of the heads of the Egyptian secret service. However, it was proved that at the time of the attack he was in Cairo and in the company of a German journalist; the two had even been photographed together.

The German police were following another lead. When the arrest of the two agents, Joklik and Ben-Gal, was announced by the Swiss authorities a few days later, the Germans applied for their extradition. These two were believed to have taken part in the attack on Kleinwachter.

The hunt after scientists had entered a new phase. It was no longer a matter of seizing them and bringing them back alive, of keeping them in more or less subtle captivity. It had become a hunt to the death. Instead of countries making war for scientists, war was being made on scientists.

When the British had sent bombers over Peenemünde the targets had included the living quarters, with the idea of wiping out as many scientific brains as possible. But after the war none of the victors had thought of doing bodily harm to German scientists. The fact that they had been distributed more or less equally between East and West probably created a kind of balance in the fears they aroused. It is very likely that even without the help of German scientists, both the United States and Russia would have eventually produced supersonic aircraft and intercontinental missiles. But the same could not be said of Egypt. *Without his scientific mercenaries, Nasser would never have been able to build jet-planes and make rocket-missiles.* With their help, he built up an arsenal of modern offensive weapons which were beyond the means of Israel. So there was only one way of restoring the balance of power in that part of the world — by neutralizing the German scientists, which meant forcing them to leave Egypt by any means, kidnapping, blackmail, or death threats.

However, the Germans in Egypt did not seem particularly worried. They knew quite well what they were doing. As Pilz once said to a visitor: 'We're obviously not making sticks of barley-sugar!' But they were well protected, and they lived in their own little world, having practically no contact with the population. They always carried revolvers, even in the laboratories and workshops of the 'forbidden city', and had regular target practice under the supervision of Egyptian army officers. Wherever they went outside the establishment, they were given a bodyguard which was under the orders of Oberfeldwebel Walentein, formerly a member of Hitler's shock-troops.

German journalists who went to Cairo hoping to interview their compatriots had to be content with submitting written questions.

When Pilz, Goerke and his daugher appeared on Egyptian TV, at the time of the Joklik trial in Basle, they were shown with their backs to viewers 'for security reasons'.

The arrest of Joklik and Ben-Gal had important consequences in that it brought the light of world opinion to bear upon the battle over the German scientists. Contrary to usual procedure, Israel was not a country that disowned her secret agents.

Atomic, Bacteria or Chemical Warhead?

For some time the Israeli secret service had been trying to discover the kind of warhead Nasser intended to give his rockets. An atomic warhead appeared unlikely, despite the apparent contact between Cairo and Professor Wilhelm Groth, whom *Alsos* had arrested in 1945 when he was studying means of producing uranium cheaply. After the war, Groth had been associated with Kistemaker, the sorry hero of the *Cellastic* affair; he had refused to disclose the progress of his research to the Americans, and yet he had sent one of his chief assistants to Egypt to negotiate an agreement. The Israelis wondered whether he intended to sell Nasser a centrifuge to produce fissionable material, but on the whole they were inclined to discount the idea. They were much more concerned at the arrival in Egypt of certain scientific chemists, among them a young woman named Mathilde Rosenfleder. Nasser might be interested in a chemical warhead. There was also concern over the activities of Dr Hans Eisele, who had been a doctor at concentration camps and who had fled from West Germany in 1958 just prior to his trial on atrocity charges. He was reported to be in Egypt, the medical officer at Brandner's '135' factory – but he might be preparing bacteriological weapons.

During the summer of 1962, the Israelis had been contacted by a scientist of Austrian origin who was an ex-Wehrmacht officer, Otto Frank Joklik. He said that he had just come from Cairo and had proof that the German scientists were working on a 'poor man's atomic bomb' containing strontium 90 and cobalt 60. If dropped over Israel, these radioactive elements could poison the soil and the atmosphere for months. Joklik averred that he had been commissioned to supply Pilz and his colleagues with large quantities of these elements.

It was difficult to know how far Joklik could be believed. At his trial in Switzerland, it was revealed that he had lied about his scientific qualifications, and that he was the kind of double agent that was ready to play off one side against another for his own profit. However, he told the Israelis that he had been impelled to leave Cairo by 'remorse' at the mass slaughter that was being prepared. This was even more difficult to believe, for he was more interested in money than anything else. He stated that the radioactive materials had not been supplied directly to Nasser; the packets had been addressed to a gynaecologist, Madame Khalil, and when they reached Cairo they were seized by the secret service and sent to an unknown destination. The gynaecologist was the sister of 'Herr Doktor Mahmoud', head of the special military projects.

Was there any truth in this account? The American secret service, which was taking an interest in the situation, thought not. But the Israeli press kept up its campaign, which combined truth and fantasy. In Israel the public became most alarmed, and there was a wave of anti-German feeling.

The problem of the scientists had thus taken on a bitter political character. Previously, despite the cries of 'Nazis!' directed at the Germans in Russia, and the indignation in America at the arrival of the German research workers, nowhere had public opinion taken much notice of the fact that the scientists had once been favorable to Nazism. But it was quite a different matter in Israel, whose people had not forgotten the horrible persecution of the Jews before and during the war. And now Germans – among them Kleinwachter and Goerke, who had never denied their membership in the Nazi Party – were once again turning on the Jewish people! Surely the Bonn Government could take away the passports of these active criminals? If it did not, the conclusion to be drawn was that some sort of collusion existed between Bonn and the individuals who were aiding Egypt against Israel.

However, in Germany there were some sensible people who had been trying for years to establish normal relations with Israel. Chancellor Adenauer, on holiday at his villa on Lake Como, sent a special envoy to Prime Minister Ben Gurion, who was also on holiday. Adenauer wanted to impress on the 'old prophet of Israel' that the growth of anti-German feeling in Israel was endangering relations between the two countries. But Ben Gurion was already well aware of this. He had shown great skill in getting his people to accept his policy of closer relations with the new Germany. On seeing the first reports on the activities of the German scientists in Egypt, he had decided to treat the matter with great discretion. Diplomatic approaches to Bonn had secured Sânger's recall to Germany. Towards the end of 1962 his right-hand man, Shimon Peres, had sent a confidential message to Strauss, Defense Minister in Bonn. Strauss forwarded it to the Chancellor, who returned it marked in red 'To be kept secret'.

But now it was impossible to keep the affair secret. It had got completely out of hand and was now beyond those who had set it going.

However, the Israeli press suddenly clamped down on the issue and stopped its anti-German campaign. Ben Gurion sent for the head of the secret service, who had been the invisible conductor of this Germanophobe concert. After a stormy interview, he tendered his resignation.

This head of the secret service was called 'the little man' by those who knew him. He was born in Russia and brought up in Lithuania. When he arrived in Palestine he joined a kibbutz, then became a secret agent for the Zionist organization *Hagana*. After the creation of the State of Israel he climbed the shadowy ranks until in 1952 he became the head of the best – or at least the most efficient – secret service in the Middle East. To him was due the capture of Eichmann in Argentina.

But his resignation was by no means the end of the affair of the German scientists in Egypt. In June 1963, the trial of Ben-Gal and Joklik opened in Basle. In their defense, the accused produced many proofs of the activities of the scientists. Chief among these was a purchase order signed by Wolfgang Pilz for nine hundred pieces of rocket mechanism and two thousand seven hundred gyroscopes. The document clearly stated that it was all needed to equip nine hundred rockets – four hundred of type 2 and five hundred of type 5 – which were to be mass produced at the '333' establishment. Nine hundred rockets by 1970 – this was the target fixed by the 'special military projects'. This disclosure at least justified the interest the Israelis had taken in Goerke and Kleinwachter, the two electronics experts who were working on the rocket-missiles.

Prosecuting counsel was obviously impressed by the arguments and proofs put forward by the defense, and he expressed his 'understanding of Israel's deep anxiety'. He admitted that Ben-Gal had acted 'with honorable intent', and asked for a sentence of three months' imprisonment. The judge gave them two months, which meant that Ben-Gal and Joklik were at once set free, as they had already spent three months in custody. The judge stated during the trial that 'it had been proved that Egypt wanted to destroy Israel'.

Now that the affair had been made public, some reactions could be expected. In the United States, Averell Harriman declared that 'the departure of the German scientists from Egypt might bring about their replacement by Soviet teams capable of doing the same work, which would bring no change to the situation in the Middle East, except to make Egypt still more dependent on Russia'.

The West German Government kept pleading constitutional difficulties and delaying the ratification of the 'scientists' law', which would prevent German nationals from becoming scientific mercenaries.

The German scientists in Egypt, for their part, seemed little inclined to leave the country. When I was in Germany interviewing some of the scientists there, I asked Von Weiszäcker what he thought of his compatriots in Egypt. Weiszäcker was a member of the *Uran-Verein,* and is a philosopher as well as a physicist.

'In my opinion, they're working for three reasons,' he replied. 'First, because most of them were Nazis; second, because they'll do anything for money; and third, because none of them is in the top rank of his particular specialization, and so can't pick and choose.'

I put the same question to Von Braun, in his office in Huntsville U.S.A. 'The Germans have already inflicted a great deal of suffering on the Jewish people,' he said, 'and it shows a most regrettable state of mind on the part of these scientists to go and help Nasser make rocket-missiles intended for use against Israel. Those men in Egypt are just stirring up trouble.'

This was the first time that Von Braun had spoken in such a way about other German scientists. Whatever may be said of the conditions of work in Huntsville today, they are certainly very different from those of the scientists in Egypt.

The presence in Egypt of Pilz and others continued to be a source of embarrassment to the Bonn government, and it tried to find work for them in other countries. Approaches were made to the United States Government, which declined to have them. Secret negotiations with France had some results towards the end of 1964. Walter Schuran and Paul Goerke had returned to Germany by then, and a few others soon followed them; perhaps they left Egypt because they had been scared by the receipt of more parcels containing time-bombs, sent by a secret society called *Gideon* which was operating from Cairo itself.

But there are still German scientists in Egypt, and by all appearances some will remain in that country for a little while to come.

The efforts of the Bonn government to recall the scientists has to some extent completed the circle begun in 1945. *It has now been shown that if a country wants to keep its scientists it must pay them at least as much as other countries which are eager for their services.* In other words, after having been threatened, imprisoned and kidnapped, scientists today are nothing more than valuable merchandise that goes to the highest bidder.

Until recently it has been said that Science knew no frontiers – but one can add that now it at least knows its price.

CONCLUSION

Knowledge Itself Is Power

The original 'scientist-hunters' have long since put away their uniforms and guns; their present-day counterparts wear lounge suits or university gowns. Europe is regularly invaded by these new 'talent-spotters'. They can be seen in the great university towns, at the doors of technical institutes, in the corridors of academies and at degree ceremonies, looking for young engineers and examining the academic careers of budding scientists; in short, making their selection.

The figures speak for themselves. Between 1949 and 1961 more than forty thousand engineers and scientists from all parts of the world went to take jobs in the United States. It is true that a good many of them had only to cross the Canadian frontier. But every year Europe loses hundreds and thousands of her best brains to the United States.

In 1957 alone, five thousand eight hundred scientists went to the United States – British, German, Dutch, Swedish, Swiss, French, Italian, etc. It was then that British universities sounded the alarm and called attention to the 'brain drain'. For the American talent-spotters had their easiest task in Britain, there being no language barrier. British scientists could adapt themselves to American laboratories without any loss of time. But the universities' protests had little practical effect. In 1964 Professor J.E. Bush and several of his colleagues in Birmingham University left for the New World.

A 'special envoy' of General Electric recently stated: 'During my trip to Europe I met one hundred and seventy-five scientists, and forty-five of them agreed to come and work for us!'

Since 1949 Germany has lost at least four thousand research-workers, of whom two thousand one hundred and twenty-five went to the United States between the years 1956 and 1961. The Federal German Government is planning strong measures to put an end to this exodus, one proposal being to prohibit the publication in newspapers of offers of employment in America.

In France, some time ago, an American delegation tried in vain to persuade the famous aircraft designer Leduc to leave his native land.

The National Academy of Science in Vienna opened a special office for the sole purpose of 'sifting' Hungarian scientists who fled their country after the 1956 uprising. Hungary had already given the United States scientific geniuses such as Leo Szilard, E. Teller and J. von Neumann, and now the country was losing many more scientists. A reception center, Camp Kilmer, was opened for them, and in six months five hundred scientists passed through it; then another three hundred, by the end of 1957.

Most of the scientists who go to America can fairly claim that they are doing non-military research. But the dividing-line is difficult to define. On which side of that line, for instance, is the scientist who is studying the strange language of dolphins and the sounds emitted by crabs, when the United States Navy is financing the work in the hope of finding new methods of submarine detection? Or the specialist in telepathy who was taken round the world in the nuclear submarine *Nautilus,* or those scientists working on lasers, which the military already refer to as 'the death ray'?

A 'new wave' of scientists is engaged on work which seems to come from the pages of science-fiction. And the wartime 'scientist-hunters' gradually go into retirement.

The *Alsos* men have a reunion every two years in Washington. Goudsmit, now working at the Brookhaven atomic center, can usually be seen at the reunions, cheerful as ever; Boris Pash, now writing his war memoirs, also turns up; so does General Groves, who has published his memoirs and did not err on the side of modesty. Other old acquaintances are Toftoy, now living in retirement in Florida, James Hamill, Von Braun's 'Guardian angel' who retired with the rank of colonel, and many others. They do not forget the old times and have many good laughs over Operation Paperclip.

The word 'paperclip' has almost achieved official status. A short clause in the MacCarren-Walter Immigration Law of 1952 deals with special conditions relating to the admission of foreign scientists working on National Defense. This clause is often referred to as the 'Paperclip Clause'.

The great pioneers of atomic science are dead – Einstein, Bohr, Fermi, Joliot-Curie. Oppenheimer has been reinstated after years spent in disgrace. One of those who left Los Alamos, Otto Frisch, has a chair of Natural Science at Cambridge. He lives with his aunt, Lise Meitner, who worked with him on nuclear fission. Both of them are leading figures in the 'Pugwash' movement to outlaw nuclear weapons.

In 1957 the West German government decided to make its own atomic bomb. On learning this, German scientists sent a delegation of protest to the Ministers concerned, but to no effect. So then the scientists courageously published a 'Manifesto of the Eighteen', in which they declared that they would have nothing to do with any project for the production, testing or use of an atomic weapon.

Wilhelm Groth, however, who was not one of the signatories, continues his research on producing uranium by the centrifuge method. Kistemaker and Ketelaar, of the *Cellastic* affair, are once again working in the quiet of their Amsterdam laboratories. Eugen Sänger died at the age of fifty-eight, but his widow, the former Irene Bredt, has charge of the jet-propulsion institute at Stuttgart, which is still privately in touch with the '333' establishment in Egypt. Hermann Oberth, after working for a short time with Von Braun in Huntsville, went back to Germany and now lives there on a modest state pension.

Much water has flowed beneath the Rhine bridge at Saint Louis since the French army transported the German scientists across it twice a day. But some of those ballistics specialists are still working in great secrecy behind the walls of what is now 'the Franco-German Research Institute'.

Klaus Fuchs has been released from his British prison and has gone to live in Dresden, in East Germany, where he found the 'red Baron', Manfred von Ardenne. In Russia, Piotr Kapitza is out of prison but is back in his gilded cage. (He was recently forbidden to go to Copenhagen to receive the Niels Bohr Medal from the King of Denmark.) A few German scientists are still in Russia; one recent returnee is Professor Heinz Barwich, deputy head of the Nuclear Research Institute at Dubna. Early in 1964 he got back to East Germany, and from there succeeded in reaching the United States.

Hellmut Walter, who has been called 'the most interchangeable of the German scientists', was for some time in England, then went to America, and is now a vice-president of the mammoth Worthington Corporation. His son became an American citizen and did his military service with the US Army in Germany.

Dr Walter Dornberger, who once reigned over Peenemünde, is now a vice-president of Bell Aerosystems and lives in the glorious countryside near Niagara Falls. Many other German scientists have long since left the employ of the army and work for private industry as experts, advisers or managers.

But most of the one hundred and twenty-seven 'paperclip boys' are still at Huntsville, although they are no longer under the orders of the Pentagon. The 'ex-Germans', as they are called, came under the National Aeronautical and Space Administration (NASA) in 1960, and their work is entirely concerned with the development of the huge Saturn rockets which will eventually put men on the moon. Von Braun and his team, of all the 'brains' hunted from their country, are the only ones to have the satisfaction of realizing their early dreams – to reach the stars. But they have paid dearly for it – thirty years of research for war purposes. Was it worth the price? All that can be said is that without the V.2s, the Redstone and the Jupiter, these men would never have been able to aim at moon landings.

Von Braun has been covered with honours. He has been named Big Chief 'Arrows to the Moon' by an Indian tribe; he is the hero of a Hollywood film *I Aim at the Stars*. At the end of a special showing of this pictorial biography, in Washington, senators stood and applauded Von Braun, while in Munich the showing of the film was given military honors. But in London and Antwerp, two cities which were at the receiving end of V.2s, the film led to incidents and was banned.

Science has achieved the most amazing exploits in this mid-twentieth century – astounding progress in aviation, the harnessing of atomic energy and the conquest of space ... But at the same time science has become the bondsman of the god of war to a greater extent than ever before. *It has brought good and evil to mankind, with the same indifferent hand and without any moral consideration.* But could progress have been made any other way?

I recently put this question to a scientist, who gave the following naive reply: 'Put power into the hands of scientists and they will undertake responsibility for the future of mankind; they will put all their knowledge to nothing but peaceful uses!' One of his colleagues, not quite so idealistic, said that scientists should break out of their own narrow circle, take a greater part in everyday affairs and share the pleasures and cares of their fellow men. They would still make dangerous discoveries, but might not then fall so easily into the power of politicians and militarists.

'If someone asked my students to construct a pipeline for carrying human blood from one town to another,' said a respected professor, 'ninety per cent of them would at once begin working out the best technical solution without ever asking themselves where the human blood was coming from.'

At the present time scientists are living in comparative peace; except for a few under-developed countries which play at being sorcerer's apprentices with a few 'brains' that they pay well but surround with barbed wire, men of science can consider themselves as enjoying a temporary freedom. But this does not prevent some of them from dabbling in preparations for war – like Dr Hans Ehrhardt, who was expelled from Switzerland for having experimented with a mysterious green death ray, and the unlucky English scientist who died from the microbes he was carefully cultivating for bacteriological warfare.

'All it takes is for a minor war to break out,' admitted Von Braun, 'and those who are happily engaged in space research would find themselves harnessed once again to the war chariot...'

A small war, and the hunt after scientists would be on again, as in the 'good old days', but more energetic and more brutal than ever!

'Knowledge itself is power,' wrote Francis Bacon. The tragedy of modern science was summed up by Robert Jungk when he wrote, 'Knowledge itself is, *unfortunately*, power.'